Editor
Sarah L. Durand

Editorial Project Manager
Elizabeth Morris, Ph.D.

Editor-in-Chief
Sharon Coan, M.S. Ed.

Cover Artist
Lesley Palmer

Art Coordinator
Denice Adorno

Imaging
Alfred Lau

Production Manager
Phil Garcia

Publishers
Rachelle Cracchiolo, M.S. Ed.
Mary Dupuy Smith, M.S. Ed.

for
Kids

Author

Lynn Gustafson, Ed.D.

Teacher Created Materials, Inc.
6421 Industry Way
Westminster, CA 92683
ISBN-1-7439-3461-X

©2001 Teacher Created Materials, Inc.
Made in U.S.A.
www.teachercreated.com
URL updates available at our website

Table of Contents

Table of Contents *(cont.)*

Table of Contents *(cont.)*

Foreword

You'll find over 1,000 top-notch websites for kids in this book. We handpicked these sites based on their content, design, and overall kid appeal. As you explore the book, you'll notice that there are many different types of sites for kids from preschool to high school. Some sites are purely educational and share information that kids can rely on to produce A+ projects and reports for school. Other sites combine learning and fun, and include games, puzzles, and activities that will get kids excited about school subjects in new ways. Many of the sites we selected are just plain fun!

Keep in mind that this book is a robust collection of great websites for kids, but it is by no means an exhaustive list of *all* of the websites for kids. As trends and tastes change, the Internet continues to grow, and technology reaches new levels, there will be plenty more wonderful sites designed for kids. So, we encourage you to use this book as a reference and a starting point. But don't forget to explore the web on your own. Before you know it, you'll have your own list of 1001 best websites!

When you buy this book, you are also provided with a CD-ROM that has links to all of the website addresses listed in this book. When you want to begin exploring the sites, it is a good idea to use the links provided on the CD-ROM because Teacher Created Materials keeps the links updated through their website. This is just one more way to make sure that you are successful when using the Internet.

A note about plug-ins: As the Internet evolves and technology improves, more and more websites are taking advantage of the capabilities that plug-ins provide. Because so many sites now require plug-ins, we did not include information about plug-ins in the individual site descriptions. Before you start surfing, we suggest that you visit the "Browsers & Plug-Ins" section on page 274 and visit the listed sites to download the popular plug-ins.

Animals & Pets
General

All About Nature: Animal Printouts

http://www.EnchantedLearning.com/coloring/

So often when students are studying about animals, it helps to have a print out of the animal with its parts labeled. This site has just that. The printouts are clear and easy to read. Students will appreciate this when working on projects or studying for tests and quizzes.

Animal Cams

http://www.discovery.com/cams/cams.html

At the home page look for and click on the link to the Animal cams. Choose the animals that you would like to see—alligators, birds, horse, bear, lion, etc. Be aware that time zones and hours of operation may mean a daylight visit will be more successful when viewing these creatures.

Animal Doc Com

http://www.uga.edu/~lam/kids/

Animal Doc Com is sponsored by the University of Georgia. Go to this site to learn about a day in the life of a veterinarian. Or, if you have a pet question, you can ask the vet who is on schedule to answer your question. Try the puzzle for fun and look at the gazillion links for more information.

Animal Photos

http://natzoo.si.edu/photos/217074s.htm

This site offers wonderful pictures of animals. First, choose a set of animals from the list to the left on the screen. It will then post another list of animals. After choosing the animal you want to see, it will be displayed on the right with information about the animal located in the box below.

Animal Planet

http://animal.discovery.com/

Meet the creature of the week or visit the Crocodile Hunter at this site for animal lovers. Best for older kids, this site features live animal cams, animal chat, animal e-cards, and more.

Animals, Zoos and Aquariums

http://now2000.com/kids

If you want to learn about animals or visit online zoos and aquariums, this is the site for you. While the animal list is short, the zoo list is quite long—more than 35 sites. The aquarium list contains 13 sites. To begin your visit, click on Zoos and Aquariums from the menu.

ASPCA's Animaland

http://www.animaland.org/index.asp

Animal lovers won't be able to resist this site. Here they can read news stories about interesting animals, submit an animal question to Azula the Parrot, and learn a bit more about the feathered, finned and furry members of the animal kingdom. After meeting zookeepers and veterinarians in the Career Center, they may even decide what they want to be when they grow up!

BowWow-Meow

http://www.bowwow.com.au/

If you have a new pet and are trying to come up with the perfect name for it, visit this site. Begin by reading the naming tips and then search for pet names and their meanings. Additionally, try the dog and cat food calculators.

Care for Pets

http://www.avma.org/care4pets/

Learn all about pet care at this site sponsored by the American Veterinary Medical Association. In addition to pet care, you will find links dealing with animal safety, pet loss, buying a pet, etc. Check out the Kid's Korner and read the pet stories submitted by readers.

Classifying Critters

http://www.hhmi.org/coolscience/critters/critters.html

Scientists have a special system to keep track of plants and animals. This site teaches that system to kids. There are five different classifying activities that kids can work through on their own.

Critter Corner

http://www.teachersnetwork.org/dcs/critter/introduction/index.htm

This site is run by a classroom biology teacher who keeps animals in her classroom. To help others who have unusual pets, she maintains this site to give out information on the care and feeding of these critters. Others can contribute information on their animals and can pose questions or contribute tips.

The Electronic Zoo

http://netvet.wustl.edu/e-zoo.htm

This site has links to thousands of animal sites covering every creature under the sun! Click on the name of an animal, and get links to hundreds of sites on that animal! (More than you ever wanted to know about cows.)

Fish and Wildlife Species

http://species.fws.gov/

This site is an electronic wildlife fact sheet. Click next to the animal to get either an html or PDF fact sheet on that animal. There are approximately 50 animals on this site. At the bottom of the screen you will find links to other wildlife sites.

Gaggle - The Learning Kingdom

http://www.LearningKingdom.com/

Enter the home page and click on The Playground. At the next screen choose Gaggle, a game where you will learn animal group names—often referred to as classification. There are various levels to this fun game.

Georgia Wildlife Federation - Just for Kids

http://www.gwf.org/library

At the Georgia Wildlife Federation page you will click on the link, Just for Kids. Once on the kids page, you can use the database of animal facts called Lifestyle of the Warm and Fuzzies. The other link is Calling All Nature Nuts! If you draw a picture, or write a story or poem about animals, you can submit it for posting to the website. You will enjoy reading or viewing the works of other kids. If you return to the entry page, you will find more wildlife information.

Get Your Feet Wet!

http://www.seagrant.wisc.edu/madisonjason9/index.html

Did you know that much of the land was once covered by water? Find out about the Silurian Seas and more at this site. Be sure that you click on the fish. And when you are done with that, check out the frog.

HealthyPet.com

http://www.healthypet.com/index.html

When you have a pet you want to take good care of it—this is the place to begin to find the best care. Check out their Pet Care Library, frequently asked questions, or the coloring pages. You can also search for information about your pet or tell them about your pet.

Kids' Castle Science

http://www.kidscastle.si.edu/channels/animals/animals.html

If you like animals you will want to visit this site. There is a message board where questions are posed and readers can respond. You can learn about the Yellow Bellied Sea Snake, the Giant Panda, Komodo Dragon, and more. Be sure to read the Feature Articles, too.

Kids Planet - Defenders of Wildlife

http://www.kidsplanet.org/

Try this delightful site. Enter the Web of Life and read the story told from a spider's point of view. Learn about wolves or how you can defend our planet. There is a variety of things to do here, so take some time to look around.

Magnificent Menagerie

http://www.ringling.com/menagerie/animals/other_animals.html

This site is part of the Ringling Brothers and Barnum and Bailey's Circus site. Here you will find information on many animals, including their fascinating facts. Be sure to check the other circus links found at the bottom of the screen.

Neopets

http://www.neopets.com/

An online community of virtual pet owners, this site offers cool things such as games, auctions, shops, postcards, and more. Register to create a pet, board your pet in the NeoLodge, and access all kinds of bizarre pet fun.

NetPets Inc.

http://www.chirpingbird.com/netpets/html/

This site was designed just for kids. Meet the NetPet kids, try the ESP game which will get you thinking, or, if you are really feeling like you want to be challenged, check out the big animal word of the month.

Pet of the Day

http://www.pctoftheday.com/

Want to see your pet's name in stars? Nominate him or her as Pet of the Day! Just e-mail a picture and some info, and your pet could be famous! Browse the archives to see previous pets of the day.

Petpourri

http://www.avma.org/care4pets/petpouri.htm

Choose from a "petpourri" of pet-related activities, like educational worksheets on dog care, funny animal puppets you can make yourself, and tips on choosing a pet. Brought to you by the American Veterinary Medical Association.

Switcheroo Zoo

http://www.switcheroozoo.com/

Kids, the fun begins when you enter this site. Take the head of a baboon and put it on the body of a bear with the legs of a bird and the new body will morph right on the screen. You can make all kinds of combinations—6500 in all—and the sounds make you feel like you are right there. To begin, take the tour to watch. It's fun!

Wildchannel

http://www.wildchannel.com/

This site offers news, features, and videos about wild animals. Some of the subjects of the videos include the wolf, zebra, and the golden eagle. For those of you interested in wild animals, this site will keep you up-to-date.

WildLife Africa

http://www.wildnetafrica.com/sitemap

When you arrive at this sitemap, look for wildlife and then click on learning. At the next screen you will find a library of animal web sites, tales from rangers, vets and journalists, and have access to the Lycos Encyclopedia of Animals and African fonts for your computer.

Zoobooks for Kids

http://www.zoobooks.com/gatewayPages/gateway1Kids.html

When your students visit this site they can find animals by clicking on the first letter of the animal's name. When they "pet" the animal they will learn even more. Visitors can also play games at this site.

Animals & Pets
Bats

Adventures of Echo the Bat

http://imagers.gsfc.nasa.gov/

Learn about bat life through the story of Echo the Bat. And when you are finished reading the informative and fun story, continue on to learn about remote sensing satellite imaging. This is truly a great learning site—don't miss it!

Bats Are Beaut

http://users.mildura.net.au/users/dgee/

This is an activity site for children ages 3-10. It contains some great projects to make, puzzles to solve, and general information about bats.

Bats, Bats Everywhere

http://members.aol.com/bats4kids/

Bats, Bats Everywhere was especially designed for kids. Come to the site and learn about this endangered species which is often misunderstood and feared. Learn about their homes, eating habits, where in the world they can be found, and how they help humans.

What's so Bad About Bats?

http://www.fi.edu/inquirer/bats.html

This site offers an informative look into bats. Throughout his article you will find links to other sites—from Batman Forever to vampire bats to bats in the attic.

Animals & Pets
Bears

Bears.org

http://www.bears.org/

This lovely site is dedicated to the preservation of accurate bear beliefs. It includes the stories behind bear myths, information about species of bears, and bear pictures and sounds.

The Bear Den

http://www.bearden.org/

Learn the "bear essentials" from a large collection of bear facts, or drill down to the details by clicking on the species of bear you're interested in. You'll also find a couple of bear games and a list of good links for more information.

Brown Bears

http://www.nationalgeographic.com/kids/creature_feature/0010/

National Geographic brings you fun and fascinating facts about brown bears. Kids can even watch a video of *Ursus arctos* in action and listen to an audio sample of a real bear growl.

Malayan Sun Bears

http://www.bagheera.com/inthewild/van_anim_sunbear.htm

The smallest bears in the world grow to be only 4 feet tall! Learn more about the endangered sun bear from this page of facts and photos.

Animals & Pets
Birds

Bald Eagles

http://library.thinkquest.org/J002383/

If you want information on the Bald Eagle, this site is the place to look. Information links include: Ecology, Migration, History, and Folklore. Additionally, there are games, great photos, and more.

Hummingbirds.net

http://www.hummingbirds.net/

Consult this well-designed site for answers to your hummingbird questions. It contains tons of information on attracting, watching, feeding, and studying North American hummingbirds. And, you can e-mail any unanswered hummingbird questions.

Just for Kids - Shorebirds

http://www.fws.gov/r7enved/kids.html

Shorebirds and wetlands are the theme of this site. Find out about shorebirds by looking at pictures, using the coloring book, reading facts about them, learning from the *Shorebird Field ID Guide* and referring to the other links.

KayTee Discovery Zone - Birds

http://www.kaytee.com/discovery/

KayTee has created a great web site about birds. Links at the site include habitat, feathers, amazing and endangered birds, anatomy, and more. At the bottom of the page are extra links for those who want information on pet selection and care.

Animals & Pets
Cats

Cats Around the World

http://www.catsinparis.com/

Follow Dalli and Sammy, two cats from Houston, Texas, as they travel around the world. This site includes hilarious photos and captions from these cats' adventures in Paris, Bermuda, San Francisco, and more.

The Cat Club

http://www.catclub.net/

Find fun stuff like e-cards and screensavers, plus valuable cat tips and information on caring for kitties. There's even a checklist that will help a family decide whether or not they should get a cat.

Cats! Wild to Mild

http://www.lam.mus.ca.us/cats/

Cats! Wild to Mild is a joint project between Friskies Pet Care Company and the National Science Foundation. Visit this website for probably the most complete cat information available on the web. There is cat history, evolution, care, family activities, and more than can be mentioned here. Cat lovers are sure to love this site.

The Kitten Club

http://www.cats.org.uk/kitten.html

This site, brought to you by the Cats Protection League in England, provides games, stories, and pictures to print out and color. It also features some of the funniest cat photos you have ever seen!

Animals & Pets
Dogs

Dogs'n'kids

http://www.petnet.com.au

Kids need to know how to take care of a dog when it is the family pet and Dogs'n'kids can help. From the home page, find the Dogs'n'kids link. There are six slides that children and parents can read together. From here you can go to the main site and read more information about pets.

Dog of the Day

http://www.dogoftheday.com/

Come back every day to meet a new dog and nominate your own pet to be a future Dog of the Day. You'll also find an active message board, a list of useful links, and other helpful features.

Iditarod.com

http://www.iditarod.com/

The Iditarod is considered by some to be the "last great race." Come to this website and learn about this special dog sled race that takes place in Alaska in the middle of winter—when the days are short and the nights are long. You can see a trail map, read about the mushers, and check on the junior event that is open to junior mushers.

VirtualDog

http://www.virtualdog.com/index_main_v4.html

Choose a virtual pooch at the pound and adopt him as your own! VirtualDog is an interactive adventure that may help kids learn whether they're ready for the responsibility of a real dog.

Animals & Pets
Endangered Species

Bagheera: A Website For Our Endangered Species

http://www.bagheera.com/

This site full of beautiful art has all kinds of information about extinct and vanishing animals. You can learn more about the problems facing an endangered species and what can be done to save it from becoming extinct. Go to the Spotlight section to read about different animals and environmental issues.

E-Patrol: Endangered Species Alert

http://www.sprint.com/epatrol/ep-endangered.html

This site aimed at the elementary student contains information on endangered species from around the world. Upon entering the site, read the poem and scroll down to the map. Click on a region and choose an endangered animal at the next screen.

SchoolWorld Endangered Species Project

http://www.schoolworld.asn.au/species/reports.html

Read endangered species reports written by students around the globe. Students follow the site's guidelines to write about their subject and include graphics where possible. A great school project!

World Wildlife Fund - Kids Stuff

http://www.worldwildlife.org/fun/kids.cfm

Some are educational, some are fun, but all of the links at this site should help you learn more about wildlife and issues that affect our planet. Get an Endangered Species Factsheet on tigers, rhinos, pandas, elephants, and more. Visit WWF's Virtual House, an interactive funhouse that teaches you about biodiversity and its importance to our planet. There's a lot to do here!

Animals & Pets
Farm Animals

Barnyard Buddies Web Corral

http://www.execpc.com/~byb/indexa.html

On these pages you can play the Gobbledygook trivia game and win valuable prizes. Then, move ahead to a page of stories of the Barnyard Buddies and meet Bruce the Bull, Gary the Goat, Randy the Rooster, Polly the Pig, and more.

CyberSpace Farm

http://www.cyberspaceag.com/

Learn more about Kansas farms from the experts who live and work there. Discover new farm planets, touch down for a Kansas farm visit, or zoom in for a close encounter with a farm creature. Tina Tractor is your shuttle guide for the latest in CyberSpace Farm tours.

Kids Farm

http://www.kidsfarm.com/

Kids Farm is about animals and people who live and work on ranches on the western slope of the Colorado Rocky Mountains. Visit this site to learn about farm animals—cows, ducks, chickens, turkeys, dogs, goats—rodeos, farm equipment, and more. If you have QuickTime your experience will be enhanced with sound.

Ten Acres Backyard

http://www.10acresbackyard.com/

Have a cow, dude! Did you ever want to know what it's like to stand around all day chewing your cud? At this site you can experience a day in the life of a dairy cow. Read about each of "the Girls," then pick one that you think could be the star milk producer of the month! Subscribe to the newsletter and get the latest news from the farm.

Animals & Pets
Horses

Horses

http://www.pbs.org/wnet/nature/horses/

PBS brings you a beautiful series of web pages about horses. Discover the origins of the horse, gain insight into the fascinating relationship between humans and horses, plus find links to further information.

Horses

http://www.enchantedlearning.com/themes/horse.shtml

Do you know what horse became extinct 50 million years ago? What is the difference between a horse and a donkey? What horse is a relative of a Zebra? Find all the answers here and more.

Horse-Country.com

http://www.horse-country.com/

The ultimate destination for horse lovers, this site provides enough entertainment and information to satisfy anyone interested in horses. A huge list of horse-themed games, a penpal database, and information on rider safety are just the beginning.

The International Museum of the Horse

http://www.imh.org/imh/imhmain.html

This museum, located in Kentucky, is the largest and most comprehensive equestrian museum in the world. Their website features online exhibits, a virtual art gallery, and information about visiting the museum.

Animals & Pets
Other Animals

5 Tigers

http://www.5tigers.org/

This site is dedicated to providing information to help save the remaining five subspecies of tigers. Click on the Kids link on the left to find Basic information about tigers and their habitat, biology and behavior, art gallery, games, and poems. Plus, learn why tigers are endangered and what you can do to help.

Alligators and Crocodiles at Enchanted Learning

http://www.EnchantedLearning.com/themes/alllgator.shtml

Would you like to learn about alligators and crocodiles? Or, would you enjoy reading a rhyme, creating a project? Visit this site for a fun look at alligators and crocodiles. Dig deep because there's so much information to be discovered.

Australian Koala Foundation

http://www.akfkoala.gil.com.au/

Everything you ever wanted to know about koalas, and a little bit more. This site has great information for projects and assignments. Plus, you can learn how to help save our wild koalas by fostering a beautiful koala of your own! Don't miss the photo gallery of absolutely adorable koala pics.

C & L Rabbitry

http://www3.sympatico.ca/poco/

Learn about how to care for pet rabbits, basic health concerns, and general information that may help you have healthier and happier bunnies. This site also features a collection of adorable rabbit photos, clip art, and more.

Everything You Always Wanted to Know about Kangaroos

http://www.nwf.org/intlwild/kangaroo.html

It'll take kids a while to read through this page of Kangaroo facts and lore, but when they're done, they'll truly know everything about kangaroos. Brought to you by the National Wildlife Federation.

Frogland!

http://allaboutfrogs.org/froglnd.shtml

This silly frog site has a frog of the month, frog radio, frog joke of the day, and all kinds of froggy fun and games. We liked the funniest frog name. Who can say "Bumpy Rocketfrog" and not giggle?

Frogs and Toads

http://www.EnchantedLearning.com/themes/frog.shtml

Learn about the lifecycle of a frog—from tadpole to full size frog. What is the difference between frogs and toads? You can find that out when you check out the Toad link. While you are here have some fun making frog puppets and learning some rhymes.

House Rabbit Society

http://www.rabbit.org/kids/index.html

This rescue organization has put together a fun web page just for kids, featuring stories, pictures, and other entertainment. There's even a mailing list for the Youth House Rabbit Club that kids can join.

Animals & Pets
Zoo Sites

Bronx Zoo

http://www.wcs.org/home/zoos/bronxzoo

The Bronx is the largest urban zoo in the United States. It houses more than 6000 animals. When visiting this site make sure you click on the Map, animals, the Snow Leopard Cam, and the exhibits. If you live in New York or are planning a visit to the city, this site will give you a good overview of the zoo.

Denver Zoo Kids site

http://www.denverzoo.org/kids/kids.htm

The Kids site at the Online Denver Zoo has two activities and Ask a ZooKeeper. The activities are Animal Scramble and Where Am I From? Ask A ZooKeeper lets you read questions other kids have asked and submit your own questions.

Go Wild: Ways of Knowing - Brookfield Zoo

http://www.brookfieldzoo.org/default.asp

Don't miss this site! You will have one of the best online adventures available on the Web. You and four new friends get stranded in the Iture Forest in the middle of Africa. You have to travel through it to get to a special place called the village of Epulu. (On the Go Wild screen, scroll down until you see the Ways of Knowing Trail Link.)

San Diego Zoo

http://www.sandiegozoo.org/zoo/homepage.php3

When you get to the world famous San Diego Zoo site, you must first choose from the top drop-down menu: San Diego Zoo. Next visit one of the Zoo sections: Featured Exhibits, Animals at Large, Plants in Bloom, Ituri Forest, or Panda Central. Be sure to view the Panda Cam before you leave. This site is a great planning tool if you plan to visit the park in person.

Smithsonian National Zoological Park

http://natzoo.si.edu/nzphome.htm

If you like to go to the zoo, try out this special online zoo. To begin your visit, click on "Zoo Views" to take a virtual tour. When you are done with that, try the "ZooTV" link or the "Animal Photos." If you are planning a visit to the real Smithsonian Zoo, stop by the "Highlights" link.

Wild Animal Park

http://www.sandiegozoo.org/wap/homepage.php3?siteloc=3

The wonderful wild animal park contains the following sections: Condor Ridge, Featured Exhibits, Animals at Large, Garden Highlights, Heart of Africa, and What's New. This site is a great planning tool if you plan to visit the park in person.

Los Angeles Zoo

http://www.lazoo.org/animals.html

Come visit the zoo and meet the animals that live here. If you live near the Los Angeles zoo or are visiting the city, the animal list will give you an overview of what you will see when visiting. Make sure you read about the condor that was released from the zoo.

ZooWeb

http://www.zooweb.net/

This is a terrific site because it offers information that other zoo sites often skip. Would you like to know how to take great pictures when visiting a zoo? Read the article on this. Find zoo Web cams, the top zoo sites to visit, games, and take their online poll.

Architecture

7 Wonders in 3-D

http://library.thinkquest.org/C008216/

This website will bring you to these amazing ancient architectural sites which were built thousands of years ago. Superscape 3-D Webmaster was used to make these 7 Wonders into a 3-dimensional virtual-reality world.

Archkidecture - All About Architecture for Children

http://www.archkidecture.org/

This site designed just for children offers information on architects like Frank Lloyd Wright and Frank Gehry, as well as information on specific structures, styles, and building techniques. It is a great place to get started learning about this subject. Maybe it will lead to a career choice!

Great Buildings Online

http://www.greatbuildings.com/

This gateway to architecture around the world and across history documents a thousand buildings and hundreds of leading architects, with 3-D models, photographic images, architectural drawings, commentaries, bibliographies, web links, and more, for famous designers and structures of all kinds.

A Love of Monsters: Gargoyles & Architectural Details in New York City

http://www.aardvarkelectric.com/gargoyle/

Did you know New York City was full of monsters? Take a virtual walk through the Big Apple and discover all kinds of monster gargoyles crouching in corners, lurking on buildings, and blending into doorways.

Arts, Crafts & Creativity

Arts Workshop - Make it at Home

http://www.childrensmuseum.org/artsworkshop/offline.html

Read through these kid-tested activities, then print them to try at home! The activities include Build a Blockosaur, Twisty Dinowire, Funky Cubey, and Story in a Box. In addition to written directions, there are diagrams to aid in the creative process.

Build It Yourself

http://www.build-it-yourself.com

There is a real need for children to have more experiences in problem solving and one way to do this is found at this site. Kids (8-16 years old) visit this site and see animated plans. Then they build the object themselves. It's fun!

Chunky Monkey Fan Club

http://www.chunkymonkey.com/

Have fun with Chunky Monkey and his creator, cartoonist Pauline Comanor. This site includes cartoon lessons for kids, stories with original characters that you can learn to draw, showcases for kids art, and more.

Coloring.com

http://www.coloring.com/

This site is just one big virtual coloring book. There are over 100 coloring pages to choose from, all grouped by theme. The colors are easy to use and the patterns are really cool.

Crafty Kids

http://redrival.com/craftykid/index.shtml

Crafty Kids has over 150 easy to make crafts for kids. Most crafts are inexpensive to make. Each project has a list of materials and step by step instructions. Kids in preschool through elementary school will enjoy making these crafts.

Crayola Kids

http://www.crayola.com/kids/index.cfm

Find inspiring art ideas, jigsaw puzzles, games, fun crayon facts, and see the official results of the Color Census 2000. You'll do more than just coloring at this great site.

Create Art - Sanford

http://www.sanford-artedventures.com/

Do you want to create art? Then this is the place for activities, techniques and inspiration! Scroll down and click the "Create Art" flower pot. Try the hands-on activities and techniques, or browse the online galleries of student and professional artwork.

DLTK's Crafts for Kids

http://www.dltk-kids.com/

DLTK's Crafts for Kids features a variety of fun children's crafts and coloring pages including projects for holidays, educational themes, and some of children's favorite cartoon characters. There are lots of printable templates suitable for ages 2 and up.

Elmer's Kidz Zone

http://www.elmers.com/

When you arrive at Elmer's home page, scroll down to the Kidz Zone link. At the Kidz Zone, you will find dozens of fun, easy-to-make projects for kids in grades K-8. Just select a project time frame and a grade range from the pull down menus and hit the "Go!" button. Elmer's Choice will find projects that match your criteria.

FamilyPlay – Art Projects

http://www.familyplay.com

When you arrive at this site, click on Art Projects in the scrolling menu on the left. There are all kinds of art activities at this site. Make clothespin dragonflies, crayon rubbing placemats, doorknob signs, and more. Children will love the simplicity of the art activities presented here.

FreePatterns.com

http://www.freepatterns.com/

This site offers free craft patterns. You are almost guaranteed a great project because of the extensive list of patterns and their ease of use. Patterns include crafts, crochet, cross-stitch, knitting, plastic canvas, quilting, and tatting.

Kids' Castle: The Arts

http://www.kidscastle.si.edu/

To get to this interesting site, click on The Arts. Once here, you can read questions written to the site creator, or you can find information about guitars, harmonicas, storytelling, or wood crafts.

Kids Domain Craft Exchange

http://www.kidsdomain.com/craft/index.html

Great craft categories make this site stand out—it's easy to find a Pokemon craft, camp craft, needle craft, or bead craft. Also includes party, holiday, and gift ideas. Tons of original, easy ideas to keep kids busy. Projects are rated on how tough they are to complete.

Kidz Draw

http://www.kidzdraw.com/

Get started by choosing an age group, then find all kinds of age-appropriate art activities. Fingerpaint, make a flying bird, create a classic "still life" painting, and more.

Kids' Gallery

http://www.kids-space.org/gallery

Would you like to view artwork created by children? This website has more than 6 galleries for viewing. If you like to create pictures, you can submit your work for possible inclusion on the site.

Kinder Art Folk Art

http://www.kinderart.com/folkart/

Have some fun with folk art at this site. The activities are aimed at kids ages 8-14. For example, you can make a checkers game board (and learn how to play the game by clicking on the link provided). Additionally, there are links to information on folk art.

KinderCrafts – EnchantedLearning.com

http://www.enchantedlearning.com/crafts/

The projects on this site are for preschool, kindergarten, and elementary school children. The crafts use materials found around the house, like egg cartons, cardboard, paper, boxes, string, crayons, paint, and glue. So many great project ideas, it's tough to choose one!

Kinder Planet's Make Stuff

http://www.kinderplanet.com/makestuf.htm

Kinder Planet's Make Stuff has more than 20 arts and crafts projects for kindergarten and elementary school students. Try making the Paper maché space helmet, or the Crayon Technicolor surprise.

Michael's Kids Club

http://michaels.com/craft/online/home

There are plenty of activities to be found on this site, many of which correspond to seasonal events. You can also browse the Idea Center for all types of activities: Fine Arts, Crafts, Painting, Needlework, etc. From the home page, choose the Kids Club tab found at the upper right side of the screen.

Paper Airplanes

http://www.phxskyharbor.com

Visit the Phoenix Sky Harbor Airport site, scroll down to the Kid's Place and click on Paper Airplanes. Try the speed glider, aero glider, whirly bird, or roller. The directions are clear and easy to follow. When you are done with the planes, try some of the other activities found at this site.

Art History

@ rt Room

http://www.arts.ufl.edu/art/rt_room/about.html

The @rt room is designed around the idea of "activity centers" that encourage kids to create, to learn, and to explore new ideas, places, and things on their own. Here, kids will find @rt sparkers to "jump start" their brains, practice "thinking like an artist," and discover things about famous artists and works of art that most people don't know.

A. Pintura - Art Detective

http://www.eduweb.com/pintura/index.html

In this online game about art history and art composition, you play a 1940's noir detective with a degree in art history. A distraught woman asks you to identify the artist who painted a picture she found in her grandfather's attic. To do so, you must examine paintings by famous artists from Gauguin to Van Gogh. Each example highlights an art concept such as composition, style or subject.

The Age of Enlightenment

http://mistral.culture.fr/files/imaginary_exhibition.html

During the Age of Enlightenment, an 80-year period starting in 1715, France experienced a period of years of peace and growth. As a result there was a style of painting that reflected that age. Visit this site to learn more about this period and the artist of the day.

ArtEdventures - Sanford

http://www.sanford-artedventures.com

ArtEdventures are interactive online games for teachers and students. In these fun and educational activities, kids will discover how great artists made their famous works—while learning tips and techniques for creating their own masterpieces. To play, scroll down to the "Play Art Games" flower pot and click it. At the next screen you can choose a game.

Art History for Kids

http://members.tripod.com/~artworkinparis/index-5.html

Art History can be a fun adventure for kids! At this site, you will be an Art Detective and travel to some of the major museums of the world searching for famous art works. You will learn about the artist, artwork, and doing art, as you complete the exercises presented to enhance your learning of art history. There is a new artist presented each week.

Artifact of the Day - The Metropolitan Museum of Art

http://www.metmuseum.org/

Spend 15 seconds to learn some quick art history. When you enter the Metropolitan Museum of Art, the first thing you will see is the Artifact of the Day. It's displayed on your screen for 15 seconds—enough time for you to read some background information before you move into the museum site. There is an archive of the Artifact of the Day arranged by month on the site.

Art Tales: Telling Stories with Wildlife Art

http://www.wildlifeart.org/arttales/

Imagine that you are a museum curator, frontier explorer, or a field guide writer. At this site, you can create a story, write a field guide, or curate a museum exhibit based on your chosen character. You will have access to the museum art and can add music and sound effects to your website, which you can post on the National Museum of Wildlife Arts site.

Ateneum for Children

http://www.fng.fi/fng/html4/en/ateneum

To find this exhibit, click on the Collection link and follow the Ateneum for Children link. You can explore emotions—joy, sorrow, solitude, companionship, and compassion—through pieces of art. This exhibit is appropriate for older students (7+) because it is written at a higher reading level.

Gauguin and the School of Pont-Aven

http://www.globe.com/mfa/gauguin/familyplace/familyhome.htm

Visit this appealing site on the artist Gauguin and you will receive on online lesson in art appreciation. Click on the oil painting and learn about the costume of the subjects, the use of color and lines, and more. There is even a project idea.

Impressionism

http://www.impressionism.org/

Take a fun guided tour through turn of the century France and explore the interesting concepts that defined the Impressionism art movement. You will learn about the change in culture along with what sparked the change in painting style.

Inside Art

http://www.eduweb.com/insideart/

A fish named Trish is your guide in this in-depth exploration of Van Gogh's *Bank of the Oise at Auvers* in its artistic and historical context. During an art museum tour, you're sucked into a vortex and find yourself inside the painting. Your only hope of escape is to answer the questions: "Who? What? Where? How?"

Leonardo da Vinci

http://www.mos.org/leonardo/

Experience the creations of this famous Italian Renaissance painter and inventor, Leonardo da Vinci. Although he is best known for his paintings, Leonardo conducted dozens of experiments and created futuristic inventions. Make sure you visit the Inventor's Workshop and Leonardo's Perspective.

Louvre

http://www.Louvre.fr/louvrea.htm

Regarded by some as the premiere museum in the world, the Louvre hosts this site. A visit to the website is not complete without a virtual tour of the palace and museum, a look at the collection, and an exploration of the Louvre's history.

The Metropolitan Museum of Art - Explore & Learn

http://www.metmuseum.org/explore/index.asp

There's plenty for older kids to explore here. They can visit the Just for Fun area for everything from discovering a dragon to exploring Korean ceramic techniques. Plus, they'll read biographies of artists, study the art history timeline, and research cultures with special features on the Met's collections and exhibitions.

Michelangelo Buonarroti

http://www.michelangelo.com/buonarroti.html

Meet Michelangelo, one of the greatest painters and sculptors of all time. This site provides an introduction to this famous Florentine artist, leading you from his early life through his final days. Here is your opportunity to visit Italy through the eyes of Michelangelo's well-known works of art.

Monet Gallery

http://webpages.marshall.edu/~smith82/monet.html

This is a gallery of 40 of Monet's Impressionist paintings. They are arranged chronologically so you can see a progression of his style and subjects. The creator of the site also has links to a site she created on Georgia O'Keefe.

National Gallery of Art for Kids

http://www.nga.gov/kids/kids.htm#

This site offers interesting activities and projects to help kids learn more about art. Check out the Lizzy and Gordon animated musical adventure or the art activities and projects related to a famous artist—like Kandinsky and Tissot.

Native American Indian Art

http://www.kstrom.net/isk/art/art.html

At this site learn about bead working techniques, Canadian Ojibwe, woodland painters, pottery and clay sculptures, and American Indian artists. The site includes old historic and current news photos, as well as art photography by native people.

New Perspective on Science and Art

http://library.thinkquest.org/3257/

"Perspective art" was the fifteenth through seventeenth century answer to 3-D glasses: art so lifelike you wanted to touch it. Artists like Leonardo da Vinci wove the scientific principles of optics and illusion into their art, creating images that trick the eyes and fool the mind. Read biographies of the featured artists and the techniques they used. You can also take a guided tour, investigate projects, and read suggestions for further research.

Picasso - Museo Picasso Virtual

http://www.tamu.edu/mocl/picasso/

Museo Picasso Virtual knows how to present information in an easy-to-use format. To learn about this gifted artist and his works, you click on the years of his life. You are then presented with biographical information and his works of art.

Renaissance Personalities

http://www.yesnet.yk.ca/schools/projects/renaissance/

Learn about the musicians, sculptors, architects, patrons, and artists from the Renaissance period. In addition, you can find the renaissance men and women who made an impact during this time of progress.

Salvador Dali Online Exhibit

http://webcoast.com/Dali/

Learn about Salvadore Dali through this dedicated website. There is a history section about this great artist and more than 150 links to his artwork—paintings and drawings.

Seattle Art Museum Kids Page

http://www.seattleartmuseum.org/Kids/default.htm

Create your own art exhibition online, discover the secret of porcelain, play with ancient Egyptian wigs, and learn about impressionist painting. Kids will gain art knowledge as they participate in the original activities on this site.

Sculpture

http://www.childrensmuseum.org/artsworkshop/sculpture

Would you like to learn more about sculpture? This site poses some questions that you might have about this art form. At the website, click on the following questions to find answers: Does Sculpture Have a Purpose? Who Are These Sculptors? What Do Sculptors Create With? What Do Sculptors Do?

WebMuseum, Paris

http://www.hipernet.ufsc.br/wm/

Begin your visit to this veritable treasure chest of art and culture in the Special Exhibitions. Here you will find two links, one for Cézanne and the other for medieval art.

White House Collection of American Crafts

http://nmaa-ryder.si.edu/collections/exhibits/whc/tour.html

The White House contains many pieces of art that are representative of America. When you load this site, you have an opportunity to see a video introduction by the Director, Curator, or Hilary Rodham Clinton. After the introduction, you can take the virtual tour.

Women Artists

http://www.csupomona.edu/~plin/women/womenart.html

This site is a database of short paragraphs on various female artists, including samples of their art, from the medieval period to the 20th Century.

The Wonderful Styles of Art

http://library.thinkquest.org/J002045F/

This website discusses four different styles of art: Cubism, Surrealism, Pop Art, and Post-Impressionism. Visitors can learn about each art style and what separates them, along with the different techniques artists use in their paintings (e.g., the use of color and different brushstrokes). Examples from famous artists are used to teach the different styles and techniques.

Bugs & Insects

Bee a Kid

http://www.suebee.com

Visit the Sue Bee Honey site and click on Bee a Kid to have some fun while learning about bees. While reading the Adventures of Binx, use the online glossary for terms you do not know. Check out the recipes for kids and the games. If you want more information, return to the home site and click on the hive.

BugBios

http://www.insects.org/

The authors of this website would like you to appreciate insects as much as they do. So they created BugBios to help you get acquainted with insects. The entofiles provides background information on the little critters while classinsecta delivers worthwhile information and graphics on butterfly wing patterns, which can be as beautiful as stained glass. Entolinks offer more insect links on the web.

Butterflies and Bugs

http://www.billybear4kids.com/butterfly/flutter-fun.html

At this site you'll find ideas for butterfly crafts, an online bug hunt, word searches and crossword puzzles, and print 'n play bookmarks, flashcards, and more. Even download a butterfly font or wallpaper.

Butterflies: On the Wings of Freedom

http://library.thinkquest.org/C002251

This is an incredible site about butterflies that has something for everybody. Information is presented at varying levels for elementary students as well as the more mature learners. Included on the site are games and plenty of resources.

Children's Butterfly Site

http://www.mesc.usgs.gov/butterfly

This site offers students of all ages great information about the butterfly. Look at the photo gallery, find other resources, use the coloring pages, read the frequently asked questions, and more.

How to Make an Insect Collection

http://www.comnet.ca/~defayette/newinsects/intro.htm

Let entomologist Roch Defayette teach you how to collect, catch, and spread all sorts of bugs! Information on bug-catching equipment, storage and preservation, spreading insects, and more. Very detailed site!

Insecta Inspecta World

http://www.insecta-inspecta.com

Join the Insecta Inspecta team and enter the amazing world of insects! This site has information, photos, and diagrams on ants, bees, beetles, butterflies, crickets, fleas, termites, mosquitoes, and more.

Insects

http://www.enchantedlearning.com/themes/insects.shtml

Visit this site and plan to stay awhile. In addition to the usual crafts and rhymes found at some of the Enchahtedlearning.com sites, there are more than 30 links to specific insects. Be sure to try the Butterfly Life cycle, and the butterfly and moths links.

Most Wanted Bugs

http://www.pbrc.hawaii.edu/~kunkel/wanted/

The FBIA (Federal Bug Intelligence Agency) seeks your help in locating a gang of notorious creepy crawlies! View electron microscopic images of bug mugs and bodies and a descriptive rap sheet for the 12 most-wanted creepy crawlies. Gross!

NMNH Virtual Tour - O. Orkin Insect Zoo

http://www.mnh.si.edu/museum/VirtualTour/Tour/Second/InsectZoo/index.html

Although not huge, this Smithsonian National Museum of Natural History site offers information on insects. If you are planning a trip to the Smithsonian, this is a good place to get an overview of the display.

Spiders

http://www.enchantedlearning.com/themes/spiders.shtml

Learn about spiders at this wonderfully informative site. The rhymes *Itsy, Bitsy Spider* and *Little Miss Muffet* can be found here. And while you are here, check out the fun spider crafts.

Yucky Roach World

http://yucky.kids.discovery.com/roaches/

Everything you ever wanted to know about roaches is revealed on this site. You'll find amazing roach facts, hear the yucky rustle of roaches, read about roach removal, take the roach quiz, and more. After all, do you know what happens if you cut off a cockroach's head?

Characters, Toys & TV Friends

Amelia's Desktop

http://www.americangirl.com/amelia/desktop/index1.html

Amelia (of American Girl fame) shares her desktop on this fun site. And what a desktop it is! Check Amelia's e-mail, make hilarious faces with the FaceMaker, get advice from the Magic Washing Machine (think Magic 8 Ball with longer answers!), and download goodies like an Amelia screen saver.

The American Girls Collection

http://www.americangirl.com/collection/collection/index.html

Into Felicity, Molly, Addy, or Kit? At the American Girls Collection site, girls can learn more about their favorite characters, meet other fans, play games, and research local American Girl events. We like the Your Day in History feature, where you can plug in your birthday and learn what other historical events happened that day.

American Girl Magazine

http://www.americangirl.com/ag/index.html

This girl power site is great fun on a rainy day. It offers tons of tips on what to do today—everything from money-making ideas to recipes for simple snacks. Plus, there are games, net pets, quizzes, secret messages, paper dolls, and many more girly treasures.

Arthur

http://www.pbs.org/wgbh/arthur/

Fans of the brainy aardvark can't miss this site, which gives kids an insight into the lives of Arthur and his friends, and will even test their knowledge of Arthur trivia in the Brain's Brain Game. Kids can send electronic postcards, learn to draw Arthur, play Buster's ice cream game of fun and sprinkles, and more. Don't miss Francine's PlayMaker, which gives kids expert tips on how to put on a play at home. (It even includes Arthur scripts!)

Barbie

http://www.barbie.com/

Barbie looks spectacular on the Web! You'll find her here at her official site that's packed with activities, fashion, and fun. You can write a story, send a postcard, print a creation, play games, and more. We were thrilled to go inside Barbie's closet and dress her up for a date!

Barney Online

http://www.barney.com/

If your child's a fan of the infamous purple dinosaur, she'll find plenty to do inside Barney's online house. Little ones can play hide-and-seek as they navigate to different areas of Barney's site where they'll find Barney stories, music (he sings "I Love You" in nine languages!), and more. We liked reading the answers to Barney's fan mail!

The Official Berenstain Bears Website

http://www.berenstainbears.com/

Visit Berenstain Bear Country for activities like "Dress Up The Berenstain Bears" and "Sister Bear's New Mystery Message." Take the Berenstain Bears trivia quiz, send e-mail to one of the Bears, view Berenstain Bears videos, and read all about the Bears and their creators. Lots of literary fun here!

Between the Lions

http://www.pbs.org/wgbh/lions/

Each week this site features an "adventure," which includes one story and a dozen related games that target reading, writing, listening, and speaking. The original games and stories are based on the TV series and all follow the week's theme and curriculum goals. The site is updated every Monday with a new Web adventure.

Cabbage Patch Kids

http://www.cabbagepatchkids.com/index.asp

Would you like to see where your Cabbage Patch Kid was born? Visit this online cabbage patch to learn the Cabbage Patch Kids legend and play games like Find my Twin (concentration), Tic-Tac-Toe, and more.

Captain Underpants

http://www.scholastic.com/captainunderpants/index.htm

At this site, kids can create a new comic caper starring their favorite superhero, then e-mail it to a friend. They'll use the Name Change-o-Chart 2000 to get a silly new name, animate a scene from Captain Underpants, and more. Laughs guaranteed!

Clifford

http://www.pbs.org/clifford/

When they visit Clifford in his online doghouse, kids can read-along with Emily Elizabeth in an interactive storybook, print out pages to color, and play educational games. We like the Behind the Scenes area where kids can learn to draw Clifford themselves and meet the cast of the TV show. Did you know that Clifford's voice is John Ritter of *Three's Company* fame?

Diva Starz

http://www.divastarz.com

Step into the fashion world with Tia, Nikki, Alexa, and Summer. This site is a fabulicious world of trés chic fashion and fun. Click to explore the girls' rooms, read their diaries, play games, and more.

Dragon Tales

http://www.pbs.org/dragontales/

If you wish with all your heart to fly with dragons in a land apart, this is the site for you! Choose a dragon to fly with and let the dragon games begin. This immersive online version of Dragon Land is full of games, songs, and other creative learning activities.

Generation Girl

http://www.generationgirl.com/

Girl power at its best! At this site, you can be a private investigator, take part in the Daily Poll, match yourself to a Generation Girl, talk with celebrities like Vitamin C, and more.

Scholastic's Harry Potter

http://www.scholastic.com/harrypotter/home.asp

This sparkling Scholastic site has plenty of fun for young muggles, witches, and wizards. Answer a poll question in the Discussion Chamber, send a quick letter via Owl Post, or test your knowledge in Wizard Trivia (watch out, it's tough!). Have you been tripping over some of the words and names in the Harry Potter books? One of the best parts of this site is the pronunciation guide to help you over those tongue-twisty words. Get a Harry Potter screen saver while you're there!

Hot Wheels

http://www.hotwheels.com/kids/

Get a racing rush from the games at this site. SpeedCity is an online game—register to join (at the DMV) or play as a guest with a temporary license. At the Hot Wheels Raceway, compete for the prized Hot Wheels Racing Cup. Be sure to visit the Post Office to send Hot Wheels postcards to your friends.

Kelly Club

http://www.barbie.com/Sister_Sites/Kelly_Club

If Barbie's little sis is your playmate, you'll love this site. Choose a level to play in the Kelly Maze. Or, click inside Kelly Castle and you'll meet Prince Tommy, Jester Jenny, Wizard Melody, and Princess Kelly.

Noddy

http://www.pbs.org/kids/noddy/

Visit Noddy's site for plenty of activities designed for 3- to 7-year-olds. Older kids can play on their own, while younger kids will have more fun with a caregiver playing alongside them. Like the show, the site has a special focus on music education.

Mary-KateandAshley.com

http://www.marykateandashley.com/

This girls' community encourages users to share and get involved. Girls can share their most embarrassing moments, rant about what's on their minds, e-mail questions to the twins, chat with other fans, and more. And, of course, they'll get the scoop on the dynamic duo's latest endeavors, including books, videos, and merchandise.

Pokémon World

http://www.pokemon.com/

Let's face it, Poké-mania isn't over yet. Pokémasters-in-training can visit this site for Nintendo news, card games, comics, downloadable goodies, and more.

Snoopy.com

http://www.snoopy.com/

Read a Peanuts comic every day at the official Peanuts website. You'll find a strip library here, along with Peanuts history, character profiles, downloadable movies, and more. While you're there, get a Peanuts cursor to jazz up your computer.

Star Wars

http://www.starwars.com/

This is a destination designed specially for Star Wars nuts. If you can't wait for Episode II to be in theaters, you'll love the behind-the-scenes talk about the movie's progress. You can even get your own fan Web page for free!

Fun With Spot

http://www.funwithspot.com/house.asp?locale=US

Home to the playful yellow dog, this site is ideal for young children. Simple drawings (just like in the books) make navigation easy. There's plenty of fun to be had at a party, the beach, the farm, or the park.

The Ultimate VeggieTales Website

http://www.ultimateveggie.com/

Lookin' to download some sounds from a video, see pictures, or read song lyrics? This is your site. Everything you ever wanted to know about the *VeggieTales* video series is here! You'll find silly songs, characters profiles, a Web club, video clips, coloring pages, and Bob's news briefs about latest Veggie going-ons.

Clip Art

ClipArt Universe

http://www.nzwwa.com/mirror/clipart/

This site contains great graphics and they are all free. The graphics include animated gifs, pictures, backgrounds, dividers, and buttons.

CoolClips.com

http://dir.coolclips.com/Education/School/

Would you like some cool clip art for your website or report cover? Then check this site out. Begin with their education clipart, but don't ignore the other graphics available—like business and holiday-themed art.

Discovery School's Clip Art Gallery

http://school.discovery.com/clipart/

The clip art at this site is fantastic because there is a wide selection. Some topics include Animated Clips, Science, Art, Seasons & Holidays, Social Studies, Special Events, Fun & Games, Sports, Students, and more.

IconMania

http://www.kidsdomain.com/icon/index.html

If you want fantastic graphics, this is a great place to start looking. There are links for sports, animals, pets, flowers and plants, dolls and toys, clip art, and much, much more.

Countries & Continents

Africa - Geographia

http://www.geographia.com/indx06.htm

Geographia invites readers to explore all the traditional African safari destinations, but the game parks and wildlife reserves are only the beginning of the adventure. The second largest continent on Earth, Africa, contains more countries than any other continent. Some of the countries explored here include: Botswana, Ghana, Morocco, and Tanzania.

Africa Online - Kids Only

http://www.africaonline.com/

Here's your chance to learn about Africa. Click on Kids in the sidebar. Read Rainbow Magazine—a Kenyan magazine for kids, play games and decode messages, learn about the over 1000 languages in Africa, meet African students on line, find a keypal, or just browse around. This site is here for you to discover new places and ideas, but also for you to ask questions and share what you know with others.

The Living Africa

http://library.thinkquest.org/16645/

This is an excellent educational site on the continent of Africa that teaches students about the people, the land, and the wildlife. You can not only go on a virtual safari, but you can also send electronic post cards to friends, explore the Living Atlas, and take the Wildlife Conservation Challenge.

Antarctica - South Pole Questions and Answer

http://www.southpole.com/qanda.html

Janice and Randy have been asked many questions about their trip to Antarctica, specifically the South Pole. Using this web page you can submit your own questions. Please check back frequently for new questions and updated answers. Categories include: Outdoors & Weather; Plants & Animals; People & Living; Travel; History; and Discovery Questions.

Virtual Antarctica

http://www.terraquest.com

Click on the Virtual Antarctica to get ready for this online expedition. You might want to start with The View from the Bridge to gain the background information needed—maps, itinerary, etc. Check out the Guide Book for information on the birds and animals of the Antarctica, a glossary of terms, and more. Enjoy this virtual voyage.

Asia - Geographia

http://www.geographia.com/indx04.htm

The countries of Asia are so diverse that on the surface they have little in common. If anything, their commonality lies in diversity itself. Many of the societies in Asia are composed of a multiplicity of ethnic groups and religions, tribes and languages. Countries included at this site are Vietnam, Russia, China, Nepal, and Indonesia.

Australia - Aboriginal Art and Culture Center

http://aboriginalart.com.au/culture/

Learn about this Aboriginal group—the Arrentes—of Australia. This site offers information on their culture, the community, and Dreamtime, what they believe is the source of their life. More than cultural aspects, this site includes information on artists and includes an online gallery. Click in the images for a closer view.

Australia - Trishan's OZ

http://www.ozramp.net.au/~senani/mainpage.htm

This award-winning site created by a young Australian boy is very comprehensive. Topics covered at this site include: Melbourne, Outback, Barrier Reef, and Sri Lanka. Make sure you bone-up the Native Australian animals. This is a great site to visit because it is visually pleasing and informative.

Austria

http://www.austria.gv.at/e/

Come to this site to get an overview of Austria. On their home page, click on Austria in the green menu bars. At the next screen you will be able to choose from subjects such as Country and its People, History, Culture, Coat of Arms, and more.

Belgium

http://belgium.fgov.be/pa/ena_frame.htm

Learn about Belgium, one of the Benelux countries at this site. This site is the government's home page, but there are links to other useful pages. Try the Monarchy of Belgium where you will find information and pictures on the royal family and their royal palace. Click on All About Belgium to learn about the People, culture, and the country in general.

About Canada

http://canada.gc.ca/canadiana/cdaind_e.html#geo

This government created site includes almost everything you could want to know about Canada. At the entry page you will find a Quick Launch pull-down menu with 15 categories of information.

Canadian Electronic Passport

http://www.mrdowling.com/709canada.html

If you are looking for quick facts about Canada, try this resource site. The first page has twenty-two helpful facts and links. Note that there are links to: Canada's Parliamentary system of Government; The First Canadians; The arrival of the Europeans; Quebec; The Atlantic Provinces; and Links to Canada on the Internet.

Canadian History Timeline

http://www.cbc4kids.ca/general/time/history-challenge/winner1/timelineframe.html

Studying a timeline often gives an insightful overview of a culture and that is no exception at this Canadian site. Click the Start Page button to hear the Canadian National Anthem.

Nunavet, Canada Photo Tours

http://www.arctic-travel.com/photo/index.html

Take a photo tour of the north. This site includes pictures of Pangnirtung: A Community Snapshot, Nunavut's Landscape: A Portrait of Naked Beauty, "Art Keeps Us Alive," and Wild Thing. In addition to captioned photos, there is a text narrative on each subject.

Caribbean - Geographia

http://www.geographia.com/indx02.htm

The Caribbean Sea is the world's fifth largest body of water. With a total area of 970,000 square miles, it is slightly bigger than the Mediterranean. The region's islands are incredibly varied, ranging from lush and tropical to arid semi-desert. Some of the varied countries include St. Martin (French), St. Kitts and Nevis, Grenada, and Jamaica.

Experience Cuba

http://library.thinkquest.org/18355/

This site allows you to experience Cuba without actually traveling to this hard-to-visit country. This site includes an in-depth tour and presents information on culture, history, politics, people, places, and current events. Basic information such as population, life expectancy, religions, presidents, and major industries are also included.

England - The British Monarchy

http://www.royal.gov.uk./history/crown.htm

The British Monarchy website was created to give the public an understanding of what this ruling family is all about. Beginning with The Anglo-Saxon Kings to the Monarchy today, you can discover the true lineage of this royalty. There are specific links for Diana, Princess of Wales, the Royal Palaces, and more.

France - Eiffel Tower

http://www.endex.com/gf/buildings/eiffel/eiffel.html

The Eiffel Tower is a beautiful building that is a landmark of France. Learn about this incredible building: How many miles can you see from the tower? Did any other country's flag ever fly on this French landmark? How many people have visited this building? (The answer to this last one is a huge number!)

Franceway

http://www.franceway.com/welcome.htm

The Franceway website was designed for travelers and those who want to learn about the country. Information links cover history, geography, politics, regions of France, and culture—including food, art, and Paris.

Germany Online

http://www.germany-info.org/f_index.html

Germany Online is the gateway to the German Embassy, Information Center, and Consulates and the UN. Information links include Culture, Government and Politics, 10 Years of German Unification, and more. If you can't find the information you need, use their search capabilities.

Greenland Guide

http://www.greenland-guide.gl/

Go to this site to see beautiful pictures of Greenland including its icebergs, glaciers and snowcaps. In addition learn about the outdoor life, the habitat, the dog-sledge, midnight sun, and more.

India - Nepal - Tibet - Himalayas: Where Earth Meets Sky

http://library.thinkquest.org/10131/

Take an awe-inspiring tour of the world's greatest mountain range—the Himalayas. Through India, Nepal, and Tibet you can study the geology of these mountains, find why many feel called to trek this region, and look closely at the environmental challenges present. Well-written with beautiful pictures, this site conveys a true feeling for the majesty of this part of the world. The Atlas collection examines the finer details of the highest spots on Earth.

Welcome to India

http://www.welcometoindia.com/

Travel to India through this exotic website. Information is available on the culture, history, cuisine, art, music, and dance. You will get the feeling of being there when you visit this site.

Information on the Irish State

http://www.irlgov.ie/

When you want information on the Irish State—Ireland—visit this website. Some of the learning links include President, Houses of the Oireachtas (Parliament of Ireland), Taoiseach (Prime Minister), Garda Síochána (Police), Defence Forces, Government Departments, and Local Authorities. But that isn't all. Look at the links located at the bottom of the screen.

Embassy of Israel

http://www.israelemb.org/

Get the scoop on Israel through this elegant website. Information links include Israel A - Z, Israeli House, and Current Events. Dig deep because there is a wealth of information on this beautiful country.

Italia

http://www.enit.it

Italia is the tourist board website for Italy. Unless you can read Italian, look for the British Flag to read the site in English. Here you will find information on regions, cities, festivals, and events. If you want historical background, click on the "described briefly" link.

Japan - Kid's Window

http://www.jwindow.net/KIDS/

When you arrive at this site you will see a child's drawing which contains hyperlinks. You can scroll down past the drawing and find more links to this site. In the library you can read folk tales that give the flavor of life in Japan.

Kid's Web Japan

http://www.jinjapan.org/kidsweb/

To learn about Japan—government, history, regions, daily life, sports, tradition and culture, etc.—visit this colorful site.

Korea Kid Sight

http://korea.insights.co.kr/

When you arrive at this site, click on English on the bottom of the screen and you will be moved to the main page where you will find the link to the kid's site. This site offers children background information on this beautiful country. For example, click on the house icon to see the housing found in Korea or the garment to see the native costume, the hanbok.

Latin America - Geographia

http://www.geographia.com/indx05.htm

This site covers Central and South America. You can learn about the glorious empires of the Inca and the Aztec, the spectacular Amazon rainforest, and the beautiful, snow-capped Andes. Some of the countries included on the site are Chile, Ecuador, Mexico, and Venezuela.

Mexican Culture

http://mexicanculture.about.com/

Visit this site to get an in-depth overview of Mexico. There are so many links here that you will certainly find the information you need. Just in case you don't find your answers, try the related links.

Netherlands - Holland

http://www.holland.com

When you arrive at this delightful site, choose your country from the pull-down menu. This is a site designed for travelers but there is valuable information for the curious. If you are doing a school report, you will find city, cultural, and general information. One of the best features of this site is the 360 degree view of Rembrandt's house. By all means, don't forget to view the windmills!

Virtual Field Trip to Peru

http://www.care.org/virtual_trip/peru/index.html?sc

It would be wonderful if you could travel to a far away location to learn about the land and its people, but most of the time we can't do that. However, you could take a virtual field trip to the country—in this case Peru. Here you will learn about the people, their country, and its customs.

Welcome to the New Russia

http://www.interknowledge.com/russia/

With the break-up of the Soviet Union, Russia became a new country. Learn about it through this tourist website. Included here you will find links to its major cities and some regions. Scroll all the way down and find links to history, art and architecture, and more.

South Africa - Global Kid Connection

http://teacher.scholastic.com/glokid/

This Scholastic site was written by kids of South Africa. It provides a kid's view of the country through a general information page providing a historical background, fast facts, and daily life details. In addition to maps, there are links to other South African sites.

Thailand

http://asiatravel.com

Choose the Thailand link to learn about the Thai culture and history. While the information is aimed at travelers, there is background information that could be helpful in creating a country report. When you see "click for postcard" you can view the area being described and you can send the electronic postcard to a friend.

Current Events

1stHeadlines

http://www.1stheadlines.com/

This news source is made up of all the current headlines from 480 newspaper, broadcast, and online sources. You can choose headlines by topic, location, news organization, etc. Once you choose the headline, the story will pop-up in its own window.

CNN.com

http://cnn.com/

CNN.com is one of the leading news sources. This site with the current U.S. news gives you a picture of the United States at the moment. You can refer to archive editions to catch-up on past news, you can search for specific information, and you can choose from the many links that are tied into other news information.

CNN.com Europe

http://europe.cnn.com/

If you want to get a slightly different perspective on current news, try CNN.com Europe. Here you will read news that is less focused in the United States and more on the rest of the world. You can even read the news in another language, if you choose.

CRAYON

http://crayon.net/

CRAYON is a tool for managing news sources on the Internet and the World Wide Web. CRAYON uses a simple analogy that everyone can understand—a newspaper to organize periodical information. The result is a news page customized for you with the daily information that you are most interested in. While the name might imply for younger children, it is really for the older student.

Current Events in the Social Studies Classroom

http://www.eduplace.com/ss/current

The topic chosen for each monthly issue usually relates to a broad topic that affects the world. One of the other features of this site is the "Take the Current Events Challenge," which is available for grades 1-3 and 4 and up.

History Update

http://www.eduplace.com/ss/history

This current events site doesn't give a brief overview of current happenings; instead, it concentrates on a few events and provides more in-depth information. There is a link to the archive of previous topics.

Lightspan.com's Current Events

http://www.lightspan.com/kids

If you want to know the latest news, go to this site and find the Current Events link. You will find information on science, the environment, weather, government, TV and movies. Some articles are written by kids, for kids. Other listings are links to news agencies.

Positive Press

http://www.positivepress.com/

Are you tired of hearing all of the bad news that comes across in newspapers, the TV, and radio? How about trying this website to change that negativeness? At Positive Press you will hear about the good things that are going on in this world. You can read positive quotes, send positive postcards, and read about new books that have a positive message.

Time

http://www.time.com/time/

If you want current news, Time Magazine is a good place to begin. There are several sections to this online magazine: Nation, World, Art Sampler, Education, Photos, Magazine, and Magazine Archive. If you need specific information, use the Search tool to get focused on your topic.

Time for Kids

http://www.timeforkids.com/TFK/

Wouldn't you like to know in a kid-friendly manner what's happening in the world around you? Go to this site for information and great fun. You can make your own magazine cover. If you want to get a quick overview of the site, click on "What's Inside."

Today in History

http://features.learningkingdom.com/history/

Find out what historical events took place on each day by visiting this site. For each day there are several events listed and links listed when available. Check the archive for previous dates. Make sure you don't miss a day by subscribing to the site.

Yahooligans! News

http://www.yahooligans.com/content/news/

All the news that's fit for kids. (After all, who else wants to learn about Sugar Ray's Mark McGrath's first teenage crush!) This site not only links to articles about U.S. and world current events, it takes kids to pop news, entertainment news, animal news, and more.

Dance

African Music and Dance Ensemble
http://www.cnmat.berkeley.edu/~ladzekpo/Ensemble.html

This website was created to share the rich African cultural heritage with those living in the United States. At this site you can see clips of some of the native dances and read about the history of the dance troop.

American Ballet Theatre's Online Ballet Dictionary
http://www.abt.org/dictionary/index.html

You may have heard ballet terms but you are not sure what they mean. If you turned to a regular dictionary you may or may not understand what the term means by reading a written description. If you use this online dictionary of ballet terms, you will see a picture or view a movie clarifying the term. For example, click on Plié [plee-AY]or petit Jeté [puh-TEE zhuh-TAY].

...And They Kept On Dancing
http://library.thinkquest.org/J002266F/

The subject of this site is dance—ballet, tap, modern, jazz, and folk—including the history and concepts of the styles. The ballet section also includes basic moves illustrated and takes you front stage to the most famous ballets. The folk section takes you on a worldwide tour of folk dance. This site also introduces you to some of the most influential people in dance. Finally, the site includes a game to reinforce dance terms, a test on dance concepts and names, a guestbook, a list of movies that contain dance as a theme, and quotes about dance.

Bailes Fokloricos - Mexican Folk Dancing
http://www.si.umich.edu/CHICO/MHN/edu/marlesson3.html

The purpose of this site is to acquaint students with Mexican culture by introducing them to folklorico dances associated with mariachi music. Students can identify photographs, listen to mariachi music, practice basic dance steps, learn related Spanish and English vocabulary, and color in illustrations of folklorico dancers.

Let's Dance Latin Style

http://library.thinkquest.org/J002194F/mainpage.htm

This site is about different Latin dances and their origins. It includes information on the Mambo, Samba, Tango, and more. Don't miss the games that test your knowledge of Latin dance.

Pow Wow Dance Styles

http://library.thinkquest.org/3081/styles.htm

As even the most novice of visitors will notice, there are many different styles of dance seen at pow wows. Although every dancer looks different, there are certain guidelines that all dancers follow when making their regalia. These styles have evolved from the old days and each has its own unique story and traditions told on this website.

Stomp

http://www.stomponline.com/

Learn about this non-traditional dance show—read the show history, view photos and videos, get a behind-the-scenes look, and meet the performers. You can even buy tickets here!

SwingMoves

http://www.swingmoves.com/

This online guide gives detailed instructions on how to perform the latest and greatest swing moves. A great study-at-home reference if you are taking a swing class.

Dinosaurs

Curse of T. Rex

http://www.pbs.org/wgbh/nova/trex/

The NOVA program that this site is based on follows the trail of legal and illegal fossil-dealing as the FBI tries to protect the best *Tyrannosaurus rex* specimen ever found from winding up on the shelves of a souvenir shop. Plus, find out how dinosaur hunters know where to begin looking and explore the colorful cast of animals and plants that lived alongside the dinosaurs.

Dinobase

http://palaeo.gly.bris.ac.uk/dinobase/dinopage.html

This site from the University of Bristol in England can answer your dinosaur questions. It includes a section on what the dinosaurs were and how they lived, as well as all kinds of extinction theories (including 101 crazy ones). Also find a complete species list and some cool pictures.

The Dinosauria

http://www.ucmp.berkeley.edu/diapsids/dinosaur.html

This site focuses on dispelling dinosaur myths. Read about fossils, life history, ecology, the systematics of dinosaur groups, and more.

Dino Russ's Lair

http://www.isgs.uiuc.edu/dinos/dinos_home.html

The site's primary purpose is to promote information about dinosaurs and vertebrate paleontology. It has links to dinosaur art, eggs, digs, exhibits, publications, and many more dinosaur sites.

Dinosaur Eggs

http://www.nationalgeographic.com/features/96/dinoeggs/

At this National Geographic site, you can go on an online egg hunt and see how researchers "hatch" fossilized dinosaur eggs to reveal the embryos inside. Tour the museum of dinosaur hatchlings, meet the modelers, and preview Explorer's television show about the "Dinosaur Hunters" of the Gobi desert.

Dinosaurs in the Dunes

http://www.discovery.com/exp/fossilzone/fossilzone.html

Read about fossil hunting in the Gobi with paleontologists from the Museum of Natural History. Includes info and sketches of dinosaurs and photos of the Gobi desert.

Dinosaur Trek

http://library.thinkquest.org/C005824

You have been called upon to visit the Dinosaur museum to catch the employee who is stealing bones from their most prized collections. Are you up for the challenge?

Discovering Dinosaurs

http://dinosaurs.eb.com/

This site from the Encyclopedia Britannica traces dinosaur hunters and their discoveries throughout time. It has some fun and informative activities to do, and IMAX movie clips, too.

Discovery Channel Fossil Zone

http://www.discovery.com/exp/fossilzone/fossilzone.html

Hear dino sounds, look at dino motion, view dinosaurs in living color, and much more. This site is the place to dig for dinosaur information. We love the Build a Dinosaur game, where you use your cursor to drag bones from the dig to a dinosaur outline.

Kinetosaurs

http://www.childrensmuseum.org/kinetosaur/

Dinosaur enthusiasts, this site is for you! See how artist John Payne uses science and art to create his dinosaur sculptures and make them move. After exploring this site, try making your own Kinetosaurs. Make sure you see the Dinosaur Database.

Walking With Dinosaurs

http://www.bbc.co.uk/dinosaurs/

Learn dinosaur facts, chronology, and so much more as you explore this Jurassic Web paradise. While you're there, download a screen saver that roars! Serious dino fans can find links to other dinosaur sites in the Web Guide.

ZoomDinosaurs.com

http://www.EnchantedLearning.com/subjects/dinosaurs/

Do you love dinosaurs? If you do, you will want to come back to this site over and over. Practically every dinosaur known to man is listed at this site. If that is not enough for you, read about extinction, fossils, the Mesozoic Era. Take the dinosaur quizzes, play the games, do an activity, and have some Dinosaur Fun!

Drama, Theater & Costumes

Acting Workshop On-Line

http://www.execpc.com/~blankda/acting2.html

So you want to be an actor! Would you like to take some acting lessons? Try this site, for they may have the lesson you want or need. Some of the lessons are: What Every Actor Needs To Know; Help! I Got The Part! Now What?; and Line! Line! What's My Line?

Children's Creative Theater Guide

http://tqjunior.thinkquest.org/5291/

Get the history of theater from primitive theater to the 20th century, a helpful glossary of theater terms, and more. Don't miss the great ideas for games that can help you make expressions, remember your lines, and improvise.

Elizabethan Period Costumes

http://www.renfaire.com/Costume/

Need a resource on Elizabethan costumes? Come to this site for the best information. There are pictures, patterns, information on sources, and more.

History of Costume

http://www.siue.edu/COSTUMES/history.html

If you are getting ready to put on a play, you might want to check here first. This site has drawing of the types of dress worn by the Egyptians, Romans, Greeks, French, English, Swiss, and many other cultures. There are links to related sites.

Learning2 Make Quick and Easy Costumes

http://www.learn2.com/05/0509/0509.asp

Need a costume fast? Try this site for a bit of information and inspiration. After using this site, you will have a fantastic costume.

Lights, Puppets, Action!

http://www.childrensmuseum.org/artsworkshop/puppetshow.html

Do you like creating shows? How about a puppet show? At this site you will decide on the characters (antagonist and protagonists), design the set, choose the music, and create the choreography. If you want to, you can look at the works of others to get your creative juices flowing.

StageAndSong.com

http://www.stageandsong.com/

The purpose of this site is to assist the student of the Theatre Arts in the quest for education. From high school and up, they can help you find the ingredients for your success as an actor, actress, stage manager, lighting technician, designer, or director. They can help you find that scholarship, that audition, and that first professional job in the theatre.

Surfing with the Bard

http://www.ulen.com/shakespeare/students/

Surfing with the Bard was created by a teacher who wants to share her love of Shakespeare with students. At this site you will find Shakespeare 101: A Student Guide, a one-page handout on the Bard's life, a Shakespeare Photo Album, and much more.

Earthquakes, Volcanoes & Natural Disasters

Beauty and the Beast: Nature's Gift and Nature's Fury of Hawaii

http://library.thinkquest.org/J003007/

This site explores the dual faces of Mother Nature in Hawaii, both Beauty and Beast. It examines four powerful forces of nature in Hawaii—volcanoes, earthquakes, tsunamis, and hurricanes—focusing on the disastrous consequences as well as learning lessons of hope and renewal.

Earthquakes!

http://whyfiles.org/094quake/6.html

Can earthquakes be predicted? The creators of this site say "No, at least not at this time," and they give reasons why. Collecting data is a key factor in earthquake predictions, and this site lists some of the signs that may aid in this process. Learn more about these processes by visiting this site.

Earthquake Legends

http://www.fema.gov/kids/eqlegnd.htm

Would you like to smile about a subject that can be very serious? Then read some of the tales behind earthquakes that people of various cultures once believed.

National Earthquake Information Center: General Earthquake Information

http://gldss7.cr.usgs.gov/neis/general/handouts/

This site contains practically everything you could want to know about earthquakes. Find the last quake to occur, read about earthquake history, see outline maps which plot earthquakes, brush up on seismology terms, and more.

NOVA Online - Avalanche

http://www.pbs.org/wgbh/nova/avalanche/

From tornadoes to hurricanes to volcanoes, NOVA has pioneered the popular genre of documentary films on natural disasters. Now they take you behind the scenes, and show you how they capture nature's fury on film. Explore a place where the art of film making meets the science of natural disasters.

Pacific Tsunami Museum

http://www.tsunami.org/

The mission of the Pacific Tsunami Museum is to promote public tsunami education for the people of Hawaii and the Pacific Region. Visit the FAQs section to learn about tsunamis and read the personal stories in "Tsunami Soundings."

Quake Up and Smell the Fault Lines

http://www.ash.udel.edu/ash/exhibit/earth.html

This insightful, useful site about earthquakes was put together by a 6th grade class located in an earthquake-prone area—San Francisco, California. Find out what a fault is, what to do when an earthquake occurs, and the ten largest quakes in history.

Tornado Warning!

http://www.discovery.com/area/science/tornado/tornado.html

Stormchaser Wayne Curtis writes from the heart of Tornado Alley, following stormchasers as the thunderclouds rumble through. His dispatches, although no longer current, are fascinating to read.

Tropical Twisters

http://kids.mtpe.hq.nasa.gov/archive/hurricane/index.html

Most people associate twisters with tornadoes, but in fact tropical twisters come from hurricanes. This site takes an in-depth look at hurricanes, including how they're created, how they move, and just how dangerous they are. Plus, find out if your name is among the currently used or retired hurricane names!

Savage Planet

http://www.pbs.org/wnet/savageplanet/

While planet Earth sustains life, it also harbors forces that can instantly destroy us. This website, based on a 4-part TV series, features essays and interactive animations that highlight topics presented in the series; video clips; and links to relevant resources on the Web.

Volcano Expedition

http://www.sio.ucsd.edu/volcano/

At this site you will find researchers' findings about a real volcano. You can read their daily journal entries, learn about volcanoes, and ask questions. The pictures are incredible. Don't miss the "Welcome" video clip.

Volcano World's Kid's Door

http://volcano.und.nodak.edu

If you have an interest in volcanoes, you are going to enjoy this great site. On the home page, choose the Kid's Door link. Some of the pages you will find include Kids' Volcano Art Gallery, Volcanic School Project Ideas, Games and Fun Stuff, Legends about Volcanoes, and Virtual Field Trips.

Electronic Greeting Cards & KeyPals

1001 Postcards.org

http://www.1001.com/postcards/

Remember someone's birthday, anniversary, or recovery with a card from this site. There are so many cards to choose from that it can be a bit overwhelming to pick one; but you can search by keyword for that perfect card. The best part is, like most card sites, it's free!

About.com Penpals for Kids

http://kidspenpals.about.com/kids/kidspenpals/?once=true&

Need a penpal? Try this site if you want to locate a penpal locally or internationally.

Blue Mountain

http://www.bluemountain.com/

If you don't have a reason to send a card, Blue Mountain will give you one. After all, today might be Penguin Awareness Day! Besides a list of every holiday, you'll find about a zillion different virtual cards here—even ones with animation. At the Print Center, you can also print out cool stuff from Blue Mountain Arts, like designs for t-shirts, stickers, gift wrapping, and more.

ePals

http://www.epals.com/

This site is billed as "the World's largest Online Classroom Community." If you want to find an ePal or communicate online with your friends, this is the perfect place. In order to use this free site, users must sign-up for one of the channels: student, teacher, parent, or higher education. Pay attention to their special events.

Greeting-Cards.com

http://www.greeting-cards.com/

Send a birthday card, a reminder, a thank you note, get well wishes, or a note "just because." This site has all kinds of cards, plus greeting reasons and screen savers.

KeyPals Club (Mighty Media)

http://www.mightymedia.com/keypals/

Students and teachers can sign up to use this site. Whether they want a friend from around the world or want to learn about another culture, by typing in their interests, students can find a KeyPal with similar interests. Users must register to take advantage of this free service.

MaMaMedia Buzz

http://www.mamamedia.com/areas/buzz/home.html

This site allows your child to interact with other kids without giving an e-mail address—they can talk to other kids through the MamaMedia website. For instance, in MailBytes kids can speak out on hot topics, or kids can join and share their ideas in MaMaMedia Clubs.

Yahoo! Greetings

http://greetings.yahoo.com/

Send a free greeting through Yahoo.com. This easy-to-navigate resource has all kinds of cards and a calendar of recent holidays and events. The featured greetings on the right side are good for quick-and-easy ideas.

The Environment

Amazon Interactive

http://www.eduweb.com/amazon.html

Explore the geography of the Ecuadorian Amazon through online games and activities. Learn about the rainforest and the Quichua people who call it home. Discover the ways in which the Quichua live off the land. Then try your hand at running a community-based ecotourism project along the Río Napo.

Animals of the Rainforest

http://www.animalsoftherainforest.com/

If you love the Rainforest, visit this site. You can navigate through this site by category—amphibians, birds, fish, insects, mammals, and reptiles. The pictures are fantastic.

Arctic Studies Center

http://www.mnh.si.edu/arctic/index.html

This site was established to provide information on the Arctic lands. Find out about the wildlife, the Northern Clans/Kennewick, the Viking Millennium, and more. There are links that will take you to additional sites.

Care2

http://www.care2.com

Care2 is an environmentally friendly site. It claims to be the web's only Green search engine,with e-cards, e-mail, events, personals, discussion, news, and shopping service. In fact you can use it as a portal page—the page where you set your browser to open on the web.

Caves of Lascaux

http://www.culture.fr/culture/arcnat/lascaux/en

A few teenage boys with a lot of curiosity discovered the archaeological find of the 20th century when they fell into the cave with the phenomenal paintings still on the walls. Take a virtual tour of the caves at this incredible site. A great site for junior high students.

EE-Link

http://eelink.net/

Whoah! This is definitely your link to everything environmental on the Internet. The most comprehensive site we found for learning about endangered species, to get accurate environmental information for reports, to search for wildlife projects to join, even how to apply for awards to recognize the conservation work you've done! Be sure to click on the Site Map to gain access to the current and extensive list of related links.

EPA Explorers Club

http://www.epa.gov/kids/

There is a growing need to learn about the environment and this is a great place for kids to begin. At this site there is a virtual clubhouse of information. Click on the "water" to learn about water ecosystems and the animals who habitat there. Click on the "air" and learn about air pollution and global warming. This is only the beginning of what you will find here.

Evergreen Project Adventures

http://mbgnet.mobot.org/

At this site you can read up on biomes (rainforests, tundra, taiga, desert, temperate, and grasslands), freshwater ecosystems (ponds and lakes, rivers and streams, and wetlands), and marine ecosystems (shorelines, temperate oceans, and tropical oceans). There is a special section—Partners for Growing—for elementary students where kids can read an interactive story, see pictures of leaves (to help identify leaves for their leaf collections), take part in a safe bee-training experiment, and much more.

Giant Sequoias

http://library.thinkquest.org/J002415/

Have you heard about the incredible, giant Sequoia trees located in Sequoia National Forest in central California? Did you know that some of the trees there have names? Find out about the word sequoia, where the trees are located, their size, and the life cycle of a sequoia.

Glacier

http://www.glacier.rice.edu/

This website is all about Antarctica and the part Antarctica plays in our global system of weather, climate, oceans, and geology. It is intended to introduce you to the Antarctic and the brave souls who are investigating that vast, frozen continent.

The Great Lakes

http://www.great-lakes.net/

This site offers information on tourism, the environment, the economy, education, and maps. Be sure to check out the information on each individual lake and the links to the surrounding states.

The Kid's Corner: Rainforest Action Network

http://www.ran.org/ran/kids_action

Want more information on the rainforest? Here is a site that gives kids many opportunities to get involved. There is a kid-generated art gallery, steps for kids to take, a fact sheet, and links to animals and people of the rainforest.

Kid's Valley Garden

http://www.arnprior.com/kidsgarden

Young children will love this easy-to-read, informative site on planting a garden. Planning, planting, keeping the garden healthy, and showing your plants are topics. Additionally, flowers, veggies, herbs, and shrub identification and care round out the information. There is more information on the site than the beginning gardener might need.

Mineral Management Services

http://www.mms.gov/mmskids/

There is a lot to see at this site. Read about a girl's visit to an oilrig or learn about the royalties that are paid to the government for on- and offshore mineral development. View the sites on Alaska, or the Gulf of Mexico, which can be explored, through this MMS site.

Miss Maggie's Earth Adventure

http://www.missmaggie.org

Join Miss Maggie and her dog, Dude, on a wonderful earth adventure. As problems come up that deal with the environment, you will have to get in there with Maggie and Dude to develop a solution. Have fun!

ParkNet

http://www.nps.gov/

ParkNet is an amazing resource about America's national parks and the environment. Plan to spend some time surfing through this huge website. In addition to links about the history, the natural environment, and educational aspects of the parks, there are links to most every National Park in the United States.

On the Prairie

http://www1.umn.edu/bellmuse/mnideals/prairie

The prairie is one of North America's great ecosystems and a vital habitat for many plants and animals. Learn about it through this phenomenal site. Make sure you do the Build-a-Prairie.

Radar's Terrarum

http://www.kapili.com/terrarum/

Earth, land, water, sky, energy, and climate all work together and at this site you will see how that happens. IF you try out each section of this site, by the time you finish you will be able to call yourself a real environmentalist.

Rainforest Live

http://www.rainforestlive.org.uk/

Rainforest lovers, visit this site. You will find all the information you need right here—the latest challenges to the rainforests, glossary of terms, facts and figures, etc. Kids, try the section of the site created just for you where you'll find games, activities, and a chat area.

Sequoia Seeds

http://www.nps.gov/seki/kids/kids.htm

The National Park Service created this site about Sequoias for teacher and students. In addition to learning about the giant trees, you will learn about their surroundings including the animals that inhabit the forests. The information is presented in a newspaper layout.

Fun & Games

20 Questions

http://come.to/20Q

An excellent waste of time. Think of something, then answer the questions by clicking on yes, no, unknown, etc., and in 20 questions or less this site may just be able to tell you what you were thinking of. It got "penguin" in 16 questions, but it took 30 questions for "electric fan." Impressive, nonetheless.

Ace Kids

http://www.acekids.com/

Ace Kids have a number of things for kids. Try their games (more than ten), the contests (e.g., brainteasers and poetry), or read kid's writings. And, of course, you will want to adopt a Bagel! (Go to the site to see what that means.)

ALFY

http://www.alfy.com

This web portal enables 3- to 9-year-olds to safely and easily experience the cyber world. ALFY is a fun, accessible, educational center stocked with interactive stories, games, crafts, activities, links to other sites, and much more. Designed with the guidance of an Advisory Board of world-leading psychologists and educators.

Ben & Jerry's Fun Stuff

http://www.benjerry.com/fun/index.html

Take the Scooper Challenge, write ice box poetry, make online tattoos, or visit the Flavor Graveyard for some frightening fun. Clear instructions and bold, simple graphics make time spent at this site almost as good as an in-person visit to the ice cream factory in Vermont!

Brainbowl: Kids vs. Parent

http://www.funbrain.com/brainbowl/parentkid.html

Sign in and let the game begin! Kids and parents will have lots of fun together as they compete in this current events game. Choose the grade level you want to play and have the results sent to your email address (optional).

Brain Quest Clubhouse

http://www.brainquest.com/

"It's OK to be smart!" is the motto of this brainy site. Take the clubhouse challenge and score an "A" in Q & A or go to the Game Shelf for brain-building puzzles and activities.

Cartoon Network.com

http://www.cartoonnetwork.com/index.flash.html

Click on a favorite character or show (including Bugs Bunny, Powerpuff Girls, Scooby-Doo, and more) to find games, downloadables, clips, TV schedules, and all kinds of cartoon fun.

Cartoon Orbit

http://cartoonorbit.cartoonnetwork.com/servlet/Home

At the Cartoon Network's kids' site, Cartoon Orbit, kids can interact with cartoons in a way they never have before! It's a safe environment for kids, and membership is free. Children can collect and trade cToons—digital representations of the Cartoon Network characters—and display them on a own personal cZone home page.

Cricket Magazine

http://www.cricketmag.com

Cricket Magazine is written for the 9-14 year old. When entering the site, click on the first sign and at the next screen click on Cricket. Try the Ugly Bird to find the crossword puzzles or meet Charlie, Muffin, Tail, Old Cricket, and many of the other bugs. Submit your favorite "first sentence" and enter the contest.

CyberKids

http://www.cyberkids.com

CyberKids was developed for kids ages 7-12. Students can read works written by their peers and can submit their own work. Safe chat rooms are available for communicating with peers.

Cyberzine

http://www.ash.udel.edu/ash/

Click on the Cyberzine link to find a magazine by kids, for kids that contains poetry, features, news and reviews, and an art gallery. If you want to search for a special subject or grade level, scroll down to the search links.

Discovery Kids

http://kids.discovery.com

Discovery Kids has created a fantastic site for kids. Try the Adventure List and go to the Featured Adventure. If that isn't of interest, look at the easy-to-access archive for other adventures. If you want a team adventure, use the team link. And there is plenty more to check out. No more "I don't know what to do" once you have found this site.

Disney's Blast

http://disney.go.com/preview/preview_flash.html

Need a secure, fun place for your kids on the Internet? This site is an online club for kids that includes areas for older and younger kids. It's updated daily and members enjoy complete access to over 100 games, stories, and activities. It costs $39.95 for a full year subscription, but you can try the site out with a free 10-day membership.

Disney's Zeether

http://disney.go.com/park/bases/zeetherbase/today/flash/index.html?clk=1010930

Zeether is a free site that connects kids to loads of Disney fun. There are links to games, activities, music, and a chat studio. Kids will find their favorite Disney toons, Disney Radio, Disney Adventures Magazine, and more. The ultimate Disney experience!

DoDoLand

http://207.194.136.164/

This is a fun place for 4- to 14-year-olds to create, be happy, and learn about the arts and the environment. There are stories to read (in English, French, Spanish, and Japanese), the environment to follow, and the arts to participate in. Authors and artists contribute to this site as well. Check out the Dragon Ship for additional activities.

Education.com KidSpace

http://www.education.com/kidspace/

Created by Knowledge Adventure, maker of the award-winning JumpStart and Blaster software programs, this online space caters to families, kids, and teachers. Sign up as a member of the education.com community and your kids can play games, join clubs, send e-mails, and more. We like the Smart Resources section, which includes cool articles on all kinds of kid-friendly subjects like art, sports, bugs, and reptiles.

Exploratorium - Droodles

http://www.exploratorium.edu/exhibits/droodles/

A droodle is a combination of a doodle and a riddle. Playing with droodles at this site lets you exercise your memory and creativity, and discover what makes some things easier to remember than others.

Fox Kids

http://www.foxkids.com/index.asp

Complete with groovy tunes and toons, this site is definitely just for kids. They can visit the Ripping Friends to complain about something that really bugs them, send a gross e-card, watch cartoons and music videos, and play action, adventure, sports, and brain games. Home to Digimon, X-Men, Power Rangers, and more.

Fox Kids Magazine

http://www.foxkids.com/magazine/winter2000/

This magazine has fun as its purpose. There are usually two feature stories and an archive of the back issues. Try the other links for additional information and fun.

FreeZone

http://www.freezone.com/

The FreeZone Network is a kid-driven global media company for kids 8-14 years old. FreeZone is kid-written and kid-driven. Sections of this cool site include: advice, sports, pop culture, brainstorm, and fun and games.

FunBrain.com

http://www.funbrain.com/

Try the Top Games listed on this site, or search by grade level. If you want games by subject, click on Kids. Do you like Math? Scroll down to Numbers and find games like Operation Order or Measure It. Are words more your speed? Then check out Paint by Idioms or Sign the Alphabet.

Funorama for Kids

http://www.funorama.com/index.html

Are you ready for some fun? Try this site for word searches (including one on Harry Potter), activities (for example, secret squares and make a mobile), and drawing activities (including one with the renowned Ed Emberly), and more.

Funology.com

http://www.funology.com/index.cfm

This site has turned having fun into a science! The site's mission is to make sure your kids are never bored again. There's tons of stuff to explore—jokes, games, magic tricks, trivia, recipes…you name it! The creative projects use words, numbers, facts, ideas, and household objects for hours of play online and away from the computer.

Games.com

http://play.games.com/playgames/home.jsp

Find online versions of the world's greatest games. To start, simply choose your favorite from the game list (at left) and get ready to have some fun! Whether you want to play solo (try the Arcade!) or against others, there's a game for you on this site.

Hamster Dance 2

http://www.hampsterdance2.com/home.html

Who doesn't love the hamster dance? Trust us, you will laugh! Speed it up, slow it down, or click on the hamsters to make them spin. A one-of-a-kind Web experience.

HamsterTours.com

http://www.hamstertours.com/

This site takes Peggy Rathman's *10 Minutes till Bedtime* book to the next level. Kids can play Hamster Keep-a-Way, Mix-n-Fix, make a HamsterScope, send a secret message, or learn to make yummy hamster snacks. Note that: "No hamsters were upset or otherwise inconvenienced by the concept, creation, or final development of this high-quality website."

Headbone Zone

http://www.headbone.com/

This Internet destination for kids ages 8-14 includes online games, activities, and opportunities for safe socializing. Kids can take a personality test, spill their guts, investigate their dreams, participate in a weekly Q & A session, and more.

I Spy

http://www.scholastic.com/ispy/

If you're a fan of Jean Marzollo and Walter Wick, extend the fun with I Spy online. These riddles will give you plenty more to look for in the books you already have at home. Plus, use the interactive game to build an I Spy picture, then print your creation or mail it to a friend. Or, write a riddle to go along with the I Spy picture of the month.

Kids@Random

http://www.randomhouse.com/kids/

Find games, screensavers, news, and more at this site dedicated to Random House's children's book properties. Play the *Green Eggs & Ham* scramble game, join Arthur on the highway, or visit Jack and Annie in the Magic Tree House. Plus, link to mini-sites for the Berenstain Bears, Arthur, Junie B. Jones, Dragon Tales, Star Wars, Sweet Valley, and Thomas & Friends.

KidsCom

http://www.kidscom.com/

Take some time to explore this fun website. Try Dumonde GPS and figure out where in the world Dumonde is located. Find a keypal or chat with a peer in the Graffiti Wall Chat. To read a bunch of jokes, go to the Just Joking Around link.

KidsDomain

http://www.kidsdomain.com/

This is a wonderful site designed just for kids. Are you interested in crafts, brainteasers, games, and contests? Check out this site and see all that it has to offer. Parents, take a look at the section developed just for you.

KidsJokes.co.uk

http://www.kidsjokes.co.uk/

Over 3500 jokes. No joke. The jokes on this site are in categories like animal jokes, knock knock jokes, school jokes, sports jokes, and silly jokes. Serious jokesters will not be disappointed!

KidWorld

http://www.bconnex.net/~kidworld/

Do you like Karaoke? Here at the KidWorld site is your opportunity to try it out. But that is only one of many great things about this site "by kids and for kids" from all over the world. Try the jokes and Java games, leave notes on the Message Board, and submit your own writings for posting on the site.

LEGO

http://www.lego.com/home.asp

Joining the LEGO Club makes the LEGO site tons of fun. Help your kids sign up for a free membership and they'll enjoy their very own homepage on the LEGO site, as well as games, screen savers, LEGO tips and tricks, and more. Make sure they cruise the Builder's Gallery to vote for the best models!

Leonard's CAMWORLD

http://www.leonardsworlds.com/

Leonard has links to more than 3000 Web cams! If you want to see what is happening at the Mexico's Popocatepetl Volcano Eruption, click on that link. Are you planning a vacation? Then check out some of the city links. View some of the well-known landmarks: St. Louis Arch, Hollywood sign, Rockefeller Center, or DisneyWorld, just to name a few.

Lightspan's LearningPlanet.com

http://www.learningplanet.com/

Learning Planet has learning games divided by grade levels. You'll find math, science, memory, and language arts games. Check out Math Mayhem, Lunar Adventure, or Fraction Frenzy. But don't stop there because more fun can be found!

Scholastic's The Magic School Bus

http://www.scholastic.com/magicschoolbus/index.htm

Things always get more interesting when Ms. Frizzle is around. Visit the Activity Lab to launch FrizTV for some fresh facts, create monster bugs, chomp your way through a maze, and much more. Who knew learning could be so much fun?

MaMaMedia.com

http://www.mamamedia.com/

At MaMaMedia.com, kids discover by doing and create while clicking. Engaging activities help children gain technological fluency and expand their minds through playful learning. They can design and animate characters, make their own digital cards, invent games, and more. A free site membership lets kids save, publish, and e-mail their creations to friends.

Mr. Winkle

http://www.mrwinkle.com/

He's fast becoming an international superstar. This website introduced the cutest dog in the world to the world. Watch the video to see Mr. Winkle in action. Plus, you can e-mail Mr. Winkle, check if he's coming to a city near you, view his photo gallery, get fun facts, and more. (And, yes, Mr. Winkle really is a real dog.)

Nickelodeon Online

http://www.nick.com/

It takes a while to download this site, but it's worth the wait. Vote in the daily poll, read about your favorite shows, speak your mind on the message boards, and much more. Click on Games to play tons (and we mean tons) of activities starring your favorite Nickelodeon characters, including the Rugrats, SpongeBob SquarePants, The Wild Thornberrys, and Ren and Stimpy. Loads of cool tunes and music clips, too!

NickJr.com

http://www.nickjr.com/kids/flash_site/index.jhtml

This site integrates kids' favorite Nick Jr. characters into games, stories, music, and art activities. Little Bear, Blue, Franklin, Dora, Maisy, Kipper, Maggie, Little Bill, and Bob the Builder all find their homes here. While you're playing online, tune into NickJr.com radio for some preschool pop!

NIEHS Kids' Pages

http://www.niehs.nih.gov/kids/home.htm

This site is full of activities to get you thinking. Try the Braintcasers or the Games and Surprises to start. Read a story about the brain or visit the Environment Art and Poetry Gallery. You can try singing and coloring at this site, too.

Nintendo.com

http://www.nintendo.com/home/index.html

Okay, all of you Nintendo addicts, here's your site. From this site you can review Nintendo games, find out about up-coming new releases, read about game strategies, and play online games. If you are really committed, sign up for the online newsletter.

Noggin

http://www.noggin.com/index.htm

The people at Nickelodeon and Sesame Workshop put their heads together to create this smart and sassy website. It has games galore, things to print-out and color in, a section where you can learn all kinds of facts (like why you have a belly button), and much more. We had a blast with the Comic Machine! Feedback is strongly encouraged—there are places to draw stuff for Noggin, mail stuff to Noggin, and ask Noggin just about anything.

PBS Kids

http://www.pbs.org/kids/

Connect directly to the websites for your child's favorite PBS characters and shows, or play games and activities right here at this sight. Kids can submit a story or joke, e-mail PBS Kids characters, make their own TV program, and more.

Peanut Butter

http://www.peanutbutterlovers.com/

Read about peanut butter. See how it is grown and made into this wonderfully gooey, taste treat. Learn about its nutritional value and try the recipes.

Playhouse Disney

http://disney.go.com/park/bases/playhousebase/today/flash/index.html

This sunny virtual playground is designed for the preschool set. Here, little ones can interact with their favorite characters from Bear in the Big Blue House, Out of the Box, The Book of Pooh, Rolie Polie Olie, and PB & J Otter. A parent's guide gives ideas on how to extend the activities offline.

Ronald.com

http://www.ronald.com/main.html

Want to experience a McDonald's Playland or PlayPlace online? Here's your chance! Inside Ronald.com, you'll find fun games and educational activities. Learn about dinosaurs with Grimace. Practice the alphabet with Birdie. Or learn some simple "magic" tricks with Ronald.

Rubik's Cube

http://www.rubiks.com/

Learn the history of the cube, download a rubik's cube screen saver, and play all kinds of rubik games and puzzles online. Guaranteed to occupy some time!

Scrabble

http://www.hasbroscrabble.com

If you like Scrabble, check out this website. Here you will find an online Scrabble Dictionary, the official rules of the game, word lists, and Skill Builders to improve your thinking. The Anagram Builder will improve your word building skills. When you are finished with this site you'll play like a pro!

SesameStreet.com

http://www.sesameworkshop.org/sesamestreet/

From tickling Elmo to making breakfast with Cookie Monster, there's no shortage of fun on SesameStreet.com. This site is filled with games, stories, coloring pages, and other activities for you and your child to enjoy together. This kind of fun can also lead to learning—kids practice letters, numbers, shapes, sorting, and more.

Seussville Games

http://www.randomhouse.com/seussville/games/

Here are lots of games for you to play
To keep you entertained all day!
The greatest games you've ever seen
To play on your computer screen.
Plus some games you print out and then
You play them with paper and pen.

Smithsonian Magazine's Kids' Castle

http://www.kidscastle.si.edu/

This safe, educational, free, and fun site is for kids ages 8-16. It features articles for kids on topics like sports, history, and travel. There are message boards filled with questions to get kids from all over the world talking to each other and thinking creatively. And, of course, you'll find lots of challenging games and contests.

Spider Magazine

http://www.cricketmag.com/cgi-bin/cricket.cgi?tpl=index

SpiderMagazine, written for the 6-9 year old, is a delightful site. When entering the site, click on the first sign and at the next screen click on Spider. Once you get into the Spider site, try Miro's Kitchen Studio where you will find recipes, puzzles, and activities. Don't forget to check Spider's corner to see what's happening this month.

Spitballs

http://www.ajkids.com/spitball/

What could be more fun than sending a virtual spitball? We found this wacky link at Ask Jeeves for Kids, where you can get a little online thrill by e-mailing a wet paperball, slimeybomb, or chewing gum wad to a pal who can take a joke.

Thunk.com

http://www.thunk.com/

Type in a message and this site turns it into a secret code you can e-mail to friends. They'll need to visit the site to unscramble your message. The scrambled jokes are fun too. Great, simple fun!

The Wild World of WONKA

http://www.wonka.com/

The Willy Wonka Candy Factory wholeheartedly believes in three guiding principles: quality, innovation, and fun! Kids will find evidence of all three principles throughout this entertaining and educational site. Visit the WONKAvision room, Candy Garden, and Loompaland for games, trivia, downloadables, and more.

Up To Ten Internet for Kids

http://www.uptoten.com/

This simple site has singing, coloring, cards, and games galore. Visit the Boowa & Kwala site for young kids or the game areas for older kids. The navigation is really easy for kids and the site is continually updated.

Yahooligans! Games

http://games.yahoo.com/games/yahooligans.html

Find all the games you know and love on this site, including chess, go fish, dominoes, tic tac toe, Chinese checkers, and more. To protect their privacy, kids choose a screen name from a list of silly names.

Yahooligans! Web-Celebs

http://www.yahooligans.com/content/webceleb/more.html

Are you into 'N Sync or gaga over Melisa Joan Hart? This site links to info-packed one-page bios of all the hot stars, from Christina Aguilera to Tiger Woods. Every celeb's page isn't completely up-to-date, but each page does provide some good pictures, background, and gossip.

The Yuckiest Site on the Internet
http://yucky.kids.discovery.com/

First there was mud. Then there were worms. And now there is Yucky! Test your skills with Whack-A-Roach. All you need to know about barfing, belching, and blackheads! Plus mad scientist fun in Yucky Labs!

Zeeks.com
http://www.Zeeks.com

Zeeks.com is a free, safe, all-in-one Internet destination for kids ages 6–13. At this site, they can talk to other kids, do research, play games, surf the Web, and much more! If you would like to block ads from Zeeks.com, you can subscribe to an "Ad Free" version of the site for a small yearly fee.

Zoog Disney
http://disney.go.com/disneychannel/zoogdisney/index_main.html

Geared specially for 8- to 13-year-olds, this site is filled with sports, strategy, action/adventure, and 2-player games. Plus, kids can get info on their favorite Zoog shows and get the 411 on bands like BB Mak, 98 Degrees, A* Teens, and more.

ZOOM
http://www.pbs.org/wgbh/zoom/

Find over 150 activities from the show, including games, science activities, recipes, arts-and-crafts projects, plays, and much more. You can compose and perform music with a virtual xylophone, devise cool designs with the ZOOM Pendulum, and play a "memory" game with a ZOOMy twist. The site also includes cast pages, ZOOMmusic, surveys, and behind-the-scenes stuff. Don't miss the Ubbi Dubbi translator!

Geography & Maps

Amazing Travel Bureau

http://www.nationalgeographic.com/bureau/

The Amazing Travel Bureau is full of surprises from faraway places. When the kids—J.B. Sara, Sam and Marisol—pull something out of the bureau, it's the start of an adventure into the past, present or future. Try the game and see where you land.

Around the World in 80 Days: A Geography Adventure

http://library.thinkquest.org/J002459F/

How would you like to travel around the whole world in just 80 days? That is what Phileas Fogg did in the famous book by Jules Verne, *Around the World in 80 Days*. This website provides information on Fogg and the countries he visited on his 80-day travels. Bon Voyage!

Boomerang Box

http://www.apl.com/boomerangbox/

Follow thc APL Eaglc and you'll scc the world in a whole new way! We'll track the Boomerang Box, a large container that carries cargo around the world by ship, train and truck. You'll discover which countries send many of the clothes you wear, the products you use, and the foods you eat. You'll hear from people in fascinating and unusual jobs. You may even see a glimpse of your future in the world of international trade!

Finding Your Way with Map and Compass

http://mac.usgs.gov/mac/isb/pubs/factsheets/fs07999.html

Learn how to read a map—including map scale and contour lines. Plus, learn to use a compass to determine direction and take a compass bearing. This site is from the United States Geological Survey.

Geo-Globe: Interactive Geography

http://library.thinkquest.org/10157/

Here's an interesting way to study geography. Take an interactive quiz. With the correct answer you'll find links to websites about the geographic area you're exploring. Or play a 20 questions-like game and try to stump the computer by guessing the right animal. The geo-tour gives you clues to a spot on the world map, then you guess where it is.

Geography.com.sq

http://www.geography.com.sg/games/index.html

Geography.com.sq is a wonderful geography resource site. In addition to many topics related to geography—rivers, mountains, volcanoes, maps—look for the game link on the right side of the page. At the game page you will find crossword puzzles, unscramble map games, 9 Squares, and other games.

GeoMysteries

http://www.childrensmuseum.org/geomysteries/mysteries.html

Help Rex, the Dino Detective, solve these mysteries: The Mystery of the Floating Rock, The Mystery of the Broken Necklace, and The Mystery of the Golden Cube.

GeoNet Game

http://www.eduplace.com/geo/indexhi.html

The earth is about to be taken over by aliens but it can be stopped. To do this, you must prove that you know something about geography. Choose the Northeast, the South, or the entire United States to begin the game. Answer the questions and find out if you qualify as "a GeoAdvisor, a GeoExpert, or a GeoChampion on Orbit's Defenders of the Earth GeoCouncil."

InfoPlease Atlas

http://ln.infoplease.com/atlas/

This site has maps galore! Choose an area and click. On the next screen you will find more links to maps—maps with more detail. And then you can find profile information—from flags, government, history, population, right down to how many cell phones are used, or the number of territories a country has.

Kids' Castle Worldwide

http://www.kidscastle.si.edu/channels/worldwide/worldwide.html

True to Smithsonian's high standard for quality, this is an excellent site for kids ages 8-16. Read articles and view photos on all the topics of current interest to kids---space, sports, travel---you name it! Message boards, games, and contests round out the fun at this site.

Let's Go!: Around the World Adventures: Online Adventures

http://www.ccph.com/adventures.html

Take a field trip to an East African village, go on a weekly cultural journey, visit a village in the Amazon Rainforest, and learn about Arctic animals. There is much to see at this site. But don't stop here—extend the adventure by visiting some of the links connected to this site.

Map Quest

http://www.mapquest.com/

This is a great starting point from which to locate almost any place in the world! In fact, you can actually print out a road map or list of directions on how to travel from one destination to another. Additionally, you can get live traffic reports, and information from the yellow or white pages.

Moving Through the U.S.A.

http://www.ash.udel.edu/incoming/east1/countries/movings.html

Imagine your father has a job that could take you to any one of four regions in the United States. To help the family decide on a location, you are going to research those areas and choose the one that you think will be best. Through this website you will find the links that you need. Have fun!

National Geographic Kids

http://www.nationalgeographic.com/kids/

This geography site caters to kids. Learn about Nature's fury through videos of tornados, hurricanes, and wildfires; read up on creature features; and find out what's happening in the world! Test out the Cartoon Factory or the Try This section where you will find crafts, science, and cooking activities.

Online Geography Game

http://www.geography-games.com/index.html

At this site you can play a geography game, find out the latest geography news, get clip art, and find maps and facts.

Outline Maps

http://www.eduplace.com/ss/ssmaps/index.html

Need a map? This site offers a variety: The United States in 1860, World Continents, United States Postal Abbreviations, United States Capitals, South and Central America Political, Eastern Hemisphere, Europe Political, European Countries, Asia and the South Pacific Political, and more.

Taken on the Road: American Mile Markers

http://kodak.com/country/US/en/corp/features/onTheRoad/

Matthew Frondorf traveled across the United States. For every mile he traveled, a total of 3304, he took one picture. At this site you can view the pictures and route he took simultaneously. Additionally, you can view the pictures as a movie or use the pictures for electronic postcards. You can take a virtual vacation across America without leaving your chair.

Travels with Miss Rumphius

http://www.ash.udel.edu/incoming/west2/rumphius/conti.html

Do you want to learn about world geography? Try Learning with Miss Rumphius. Although this activity was designed for teams of students, the solo learner can benefit from the resources and the learning experience available at this site.

USA State Flags, Facts, Songs, Maps and Symbols

http://www.imagesoft.net/flags/usstate1.html

Click on the abbreviation for your state to see images of your state's flags, maps, and other information about states and symbols!

USA State Map/Quiz Printouts and Answers

http://www.enchantedlearning.com/usa/statesbw/

Calling all fifth graders! Are you learning states and capitals? This is the place to expand your knowledge. Click on a state and a map will appear along with questions that pertain to the map. Maps and questions are printable.

Girls

Amelia's Desktop

http://www.americangirl.com/amelia/desktop/index1.html

Amelia (of American Girl fame) shares her desktop on this fun site. And what a desktop it is! Check Amelia's e-mail, make hilarious faces with the FaceMaker, get advice from the Magic Washing Machine (think Magic 8 Ball with longer answers!), download goodies like an Amelia screen saver, and more.

The American Girls Collection

http://www.americangirl.com/collection/collection/index.html

Into Felicity, Molly, Addy, or Kit? At the American Girls Collection site, girls can learn more about their favorite characters, meet other fans, play games, and research local American Girl events. We like the Your Day in History feature, where it's fun to plug in your birthday and learn what other historical events happened that day.

American Girl Magazine

http://www.americangirl.com/ag/index.html

This girl power site is great fun on a rainy day. It offers tons of tips on what to do today—everything from money making ideas to recipes for simple snacks. Plus, there are games, net pets, quizzes, secret messages, paper dolls, and many more girly treasures.

Barbie

http://www.barbie.com/

Barbie looks spectacular on the Web! You'll find her here at her official site that's packed with activities, fashion, and fun. You can write a story, send a postcard, print a creation, play games, and more. We were thrilled to go inside Barbie's closet and dress her up for a date!

CosmoGirl

http://www.cosmogirl.com/

This magazine, a relative of the famed Cosmopolitan, has been designed just for teen girls. In addition to the usual columns, you can find information on modeling requirements, contributing to the magazine (teen contributors arc chosen twice a year), submitting a room makeover, and so much more.

Diva Starz

http://www.divastarz.com

Step into the fashion world with Tia, Nikki, Alexa, and Summer. This site is a fabulicious world of trés chic fashion and fun. Click to explore the girls' rooms, read their diaries, play games, and more.

Generation Girl

http://www.generationgirl.com/

Girl power at its best! At this site, you can be a private investigator, take part in the Daily Poll, match yourself to a Generation Girl, talk with celebrities like Vitamin C, and more.

G.I.R.L.

http://worldkids.net/girl/

If you are a girl and want a female penpal, try this site. It has been designed for girls from ages 8-14 and it enjoys an international membership.

Girl's Life

http://www.girlslife.com/

If you are interested in girl stuff, visit this site. Subscribe to the magazine, or take advantage of the free stuff on the site. For instance, sign-up for free e-mail for life. Get a snail-mail or an e-mail pen pal, or get a pen pal without giving your e-mail address away. Another option is to join the discussion board and meet other girls.

GirlsRCool.com

http://www.girlsrcool.com/

This website is packed with stuff for girls ages 7-12. It includes links to fashion, sports, books, games, movies, music, poetry, inspiring thoughts, and more.

Girl Scouts of the USA

http://www.gsusa.org/

This helpful site contains the latest news about the organization, troops, girls and more. Girl Scouts will want to visit the Just for Girls area where they can chat, ask questions, get information on badges, and much more.

GirlStart

http://girlstart.org

This organization's purpose is to help empower girls in math, science, engineering, and technology. Some of the information is about a local club but if you click on Smart Stuff or Fun and Games, you will find some interesting activities.

Girl Tech

http://www.girltech.com

This site is dedicated to girls. Here you will find sports information, articles on famous girls and women, a "chick chat," the Game Café, girl news, and more. On your first visit to the site, we suggest taking the site tour.

GirlZone

http://www.girlzone.com

There is something for every girl at this site. Do you want to know about fashion, sports, games, life, music, or books? This is the place for you. Check out their polls and surveys. They have an endless list of games, too.

Mary-KateandAshley.com

http://www.marykateandashley.com

This girls' community encourages users to share and get involved. Girls can share their most embarrassing moments, rant about what's on their minds, e-mail questions to the twins, chat with other fans, and more. And, of course, they'll get the scoop on the dynamic duo's latest endeavors, including books, videos, and merchandise.

Women's Soccer World Magazine

http://www.womensoccer.com

A great source for information about soccer, this magazine is devoted to the female aspect of this popuar sport. You may also want to want to click on Girls Soccer World where you will find information on girls' teams, training tips, college teams and camps. There is so much to see that it all can't be listed here.

Government

America Rock

http://genxtvland.simplenet.com/SchoolHouseRock/america.hts?hi

This site has set history to music. The songs/information include: "No More Kings—The Founding of America," "The Great American Melting Pot—The Ethnic Diversity of America," "Sufferin' Till Suffrage—Women's Right to Vote," "I'm Just a Bill—How a Bill Becomes a Law," "Three Ring Government—The Three Branches of Government," and more.

Ben's Guide to the U.S. Government

http://bensguide.gpo.gov/

Do you want to learn more about the government of the United States? Great! Pick your grade level (K-2, 3-5, 6-8, and 9-12) and go. You can read the Constitution or the Bill of Rights, find out about symbols of the United States, bone up on the election process, and learn how laws are made.

The Capitol Gallery

http://www.congresslink.org/capitol.html

To get an idea of what Washington D.C. and the government buildings are really like, go to the Capitol Gallery. Click on each picture to get an enlarged view.

Constitution for the United States of America

http://constitution.by.net/

"We the people…" Familiar words? They are from the Constitution of the United States of America. If you need a copy of the Constitution, you can print it off from this site. Also there are links to the Bill of Rights, the Amendments, and the State Constitutions.

Department of Justice Kids and Youth

http://www.usdoj.gov/kidspage/

This is a useful site because it covers so many areas. Some of the subjects include Internet safety, inside the courtroom, crime prevention, Federal Bureau of Investigation, civil rights, and more. There are pages for parents and teachers, too. Some subjects are appropriately divided by grade level.

Embassy.org

http://www.embassy.org/

There are many foreign embassies in the Washington D.C. area and this website provides links to all those online. For instance, you can find embassies from Afghanistan to Zimbabwe with many in between. To get an understanding of the embassies and what they represent, click on Embassy Row Tour.

FBI Kids Page

http://www.fbi.gov/kids/k5th/kidsk5th.htm

Kids can learn about the Federal Bureau of Investigation (FBI) through this helpful site. They will find out how the FBI dogs are trained and used. There are games to play and a virtual field trip to take.

History of the U.S. Capitol

http://www.aoc.gov/history/capchron.htm

Here is a timeline of the Capitol and links for capitol sites. Be sure to take the picture tour under Architectural Features and Historic Spaces in the U.S. Capitol.

How the Senate Works

http://www.senate.gov/learning/index.cfm

Learn about the United States Senate through this government site. Additional information found here includes an extensive glossary of terms, Frequently Asked Questions (FAQs), the history of current and former Senators, and much more.

National Archives and Records Administration

http://www.nara.gov/nara/welcome.html

NARA is an independent Federal agency that helps preserve our nation's history by overseeing the management of all Federal records. Some of the documents found here include The Emancipation Proclamation, Apollo 11 Flight Plan, and The North Atlantic Treaty. Other articles of preservation include an exhibit of "When Nixon met Elvis."

Oyez, Oyez, Oyez

http://oyez.nwu.edu/

If you are interested in the United States Supreme Court, this is the supreme place for information. Find out about the justices, read about cases, or take a virtual tour of the incredible Supreme Court building.

POTUS Presidents of the United States

http://www.ipl.org/ref/POTUS/

This site contains a wealth of information on the presidents of the United States. Would you like to know about their cabinets, how many votes they received, or significant events during their administrations? In addition to this information, links to biographical sites are available.

Project Vote Smart

http://www.vote-smart.org/

If you are wondering about some of the candidates who are running for office, then this website will be of help. You can find information on the candidates' backgrounds, issue positions, voting records, campaign finances, and performance evaluations made by 100 liberal to conservative special interest groups.

Rock the Vote

http://www.rockthevote.org/rockthevoteasp/rtventrypage.asp

Are you concerned about the voting process in America? This website is trying to make a difference in voting processes by informing young people about voting. There is an online petition you can sign pertaining to democratic voting rights.

Social Security

http://www.ssa.gov/kids/kids.htm

Just like taxes, Social Security takes money out of paychecks, and this site explains where it goes and why. Click on an animal on the screen and it will tell a story and give a moral. For instance, there is an abbreviated version of the Tortoise and the Hare.

STAWRS Kids

http://www.tax.gov/kids/

The STAWRS (Simplified Tax and Wage Reporting System) Kids page was developed as part of a Presidential Initiative to make government more understandable to children. It presents information in a fun and easy-to-follow format, and explains why you pay taxes.

THOMAS: Legislative Information on the Internet

http://thomas.loc.gov/

The 104th Congress wanted to make Federal legislative information freely available to the Internet public. So THOMAS was born. Here you will find scheduling information on the House of Representatives and the Senate. Also explore information on bills, the voting of representatives, and committee news.

The Treasury Page for Kids

http://www.treas.gov/kids/

You can begin your visit at this site by taking a virtual tour of the Treasury building. Next you can read about the history of the Treasury which includes information on the secret service, Mint history, and the history of taxes.

This Nation

http://www.thisnation.com/

If you need information on the American government and politics, this site is one of the most comprehensive on the Internet. You will find a library of information (e.g., Articles of Confederation, Thanksgiving Proclamation), a glossary, pictures, and an online textbook.

United States Legislative Branch

http://lcweb.loc.gov/global/legislative/congress.html

Almost every link for the Legislative Branch of the government can be found on this site. For example, you will find Members of Congress, Committees of Congress, Congressional Schedules, House and Senate Rules, Roll Call Votes, and more.

United States Secret Service

http://www.treas.gov/usss/home.htm

Learn about the Secret Service and all its responsibilities. Information is provided about the training requirements, and the path to being a secret service agent. Information on credit protection and privacy is also available here.

US Census Bureau

http://www.census.gov/

There's lots of information here. Get statistical information on People (Estimates, Projections, International, Income, Poverty, Genealogy, Housing), Business (Economic Census, Government, NAICS, Foreign Trade), Geography (Maps, TIGER, Gazetteer), and more. (Definitely a site for older students.)

US Executive Branch Websites

http://lcweb.loc.gov/global/executive/fed.html

Just about every link from the Executive Branch of the government can be found on this site. For example, you will find the Executive Office of the President (EOP), White House, National Security Council (NSC), Office of The First Lady, President's Council on Sustainable Development, Department of Agriculture (USDA), Department of Commerce, and Department of Defense (DOD).

The U.S. House Of Representatives Educational Resources

http://www.house.gov/house/Educat.html

This site is a great resource of government information. Learn how a bill is passed. Read the Constitution of the United States, the Declaration of Independence, or Congressional Documents and Debates, 1789-1873. Click on the Historical Information link and be prepared to find more!

History
General

Afro-American KidZone

http://www.afroam.org/children/children.html

This Afro-American site, designed just for kids, contains activities and information that will certainly engage them. Try the myths and fables from around the world. The BrainTeasers include a Black History Quiz, African Animals, and Zodiac Maniac. Make sure you see Discover Africa where you will learn about the countries, geography, and the people.

A Look Into the Past

http://www.ash.udel.edu/ash/exhibit/okinawa/

Edward Schwartz took pictures in Okinawa during World War II. At first these were just pictures of people in another country, but now they have come to symbolize the people caught in the middle. Take a look at the pictures and get a new perspective on war.

American Folk: people, folklore and popular culture

http://www.americanfolk.com/

How would you describe American culture? Check out this American Folk and get some new insights. On this site you will find articles about Americans from all walks of life. You will find recipes to real American cooking. One of the highlights is the Roadtrip section.

America Rock

http://genxtvland.simplenet.com/SchoolHouseRock/america.hts?hi

This site has set history to music. The songs/information include: "No More Kings—The Founding of America," "The Great American Melting Pot—The Ethnic Diversity of America," "Sufferin' Till Suffrage—Women's Right to Vote," "I'm Just a Bill—How a Bill Becomes a Law," "Three Ring Government—The Three Branches of Government," and more.

Ancient Africa

http://www.penncharter.com/Student/africa

This Ancient Africa website presents lots of information on this wonderful and often mysterious culture. The categories of information include: Culture, Daily Life, Geography, Government, Industry, and Social Level.

Ancient Egypt

http://www.ash.udel.edu/ash/exhibit/Egypt/frame.html

Egypt is a fascinating country and this site captures that fascination. Some of the many topics covered include the Rosetta Stone, Mummies, Famous Pharohs, and the Sphinx. This site is very comprehensive and includes additional links on Egypt.

Art of Ancient Egypt: A Web Resource

http://www.metmuseum.org/explore/newegypt/htm/a_index.htm

Art played a central role in Ancient Egypt and through this exhibit, you will learn about Ancient Egyptian Beliefs, Looking at Egyptian Art, and The Story of the Collection. Be sure to check out the plentiful resources.

BC Archives Time Machine

http://www.bcarchives.gov.bc.ca/exhibits/timemach

The purpose of the Time Machine is to provide accessibility to British Columbia historical documents, images, and other multimedia information in a format designed for school-age children. Topics of this site include families, communities, First Nation's art, cariboo Gold Rush, multiculturalism, and more.

Black History Hotlist

http://www.kn.pacbell.com/wired/BHM/bh_hotlist.html

This hotlist contains an assortment of interesting sites. In fact, if you have an assignment that requires information on African-American issues and events, this is the place to begin your research. Resource topics include Black History Month, Slavery & History, Leaders, News, Poetry, and more.

Black History

http://www.philly.com/packages/history/

This site is a great place to start if you want to know more about the history of black Americans. The site is arranged by categories that include news, people, life, arts, politics, sports, and science.

Captain Cook: Voyage of Discovery

http://www.hunterian.gla.ac.uk/HuntMus/cook/

Captain Cook was a well-known explorer of the South Pacific. Because his voyages were scientific, he studied the new places he encountered and brought back plants, flowers, and many other things. When you visit this site you will be able to see the routes traveled by Cook and his crew.

Celebrating America's Freedoms

http://www.va.gov/pubaff/celebAm/

This group of essays about the country's most familiar national symbols, customs and observances may be used by elementary and high school teachers as handouts to students and as curricular background material in connection with patriotic observances such as Veterans Day. A description of possible school activities is included.

Colonial Kids: A Celebration of Life in Southeastern Pennsylvania in the 1700's

http://library.thinkquest.org/J002611F/

Colonial Kids is an exploration of colonial times in Southeastern Pennsylvania. Life as a colonist is uniquely presented through the eyes of children who lived during this period of American history. Their daily routines, schooling, home life, and recreation are brought to life with stories and facts as told by the children who would have experienced them.

Comparison of the First Nations People of Canada

http://www.camosun.bc.ca/~conklin/pages/martin/index.htm

The native peoples of Canada are all distinct, but some groups have similarities. This site explores the similarities and differences of the Haida, Blackfoot, Iroquois, and the Inuit. It is helpful to read the instructions for this site to get navigation tips.

Dig: Adventures in Archaeology

http://library.thinkquest.org/J001645/

Everyone loves to dig for buried treasure! This site unearths information about the scientists who search for the most exciting treasure of all: the mysterious past of our civilization! Most appropriate for kids in grades 5-8, children learn about the relevance of archaeology and the methods used by archaeologists in their search to understand the past.

Ellis Island and Angel Island

http://www.internationalchannel.com/education/

Ellis Island, which opened in 1892, welcomed millions of immigrants to the United States until 1954. Another major point of entry to the United States, Angel Island (1910-1940), was located in San Francisco Bay, California. Come to this site to understand what it was like to enter the United States through these islands.

Explorers of the Millennium

http://tqjunior.thinkquest.org/4034/

"Explorers of the Millennium," provides a wealth of information about the most important explorers of the past thousand years in a simple, easy-to-use format. Read reports on 19 explorers and visit related resource links. Take a quiz or nominate an explorer to the Explorers' Hall of Fame.

Gallery of Achievement

http://www.achievement.org/

Looking for a website that could change your life? Here it is—the Gallery of Achievement. In selecting people for the Gallery of Achievers, this site focuses on individuals who have shaped the twentieth century by their accomplishments. Search for leaders through qualities like persistence, vision, or courage. How about searching for leaders in the public service, science, or art world?

The Great American Landmark Adventure

http://www2.cr.nps.gov/pad/adventure/landmark.htm

The Great American Landmarks Adventure takes you on a fabulous trip through time and space through a series of drawings by Roxie Munro. You'll see 43 National Historic Landmarks and learn about more than 3,000 years of our country's past! Travel has been arranged by Heritage Preservation Services, National Park Service.

Heard Museum

http://www.heard.org/index.html

This site presents information on the Native people and their cultural heritage, with emphasis on the traditional cultures of the Greater Southwest and on the evolving Native American Fine Art Movement. Read about their current and past exhibits.

The History Channel

http://www.historychannel.com/index.html

Do you need information on an historical event? Search for your topic using the search capabilities of this incredible history site. Information is in abundance if you take the time to look at this e-magazine-like format.

The History Place

http://www.historyplace.com/index.html

Are you doing research in history? This is another starting point to find information for your topic. You can start your research by going through the topical information. You might want to look at the Frequently Asked Questions to find helpful information.

In the Times of the Old One

http://www.sbcss.k12.ca.us/sbcss/services/educational/cctechnology/webquest/oldones.html

The task: explore and experience the Navajo Indians' close relationship with the land they lived on. To do this you must identify why the Navajo wrote legends about the environment, and how they told their stories in their rugs and blankets. Next, you'll design a geometric rug pattern to symbolize a natural resource or part of the environment in your area. Finally, you can create a legend about how that environmental object came into being.

Kids' Castle History

http://www.kidscastle.si.edu/channels/history/history.html

Have you wondered about the Post Office stagecoach, the Titanic, or a car that was ahead of its time? Visit this site! You can take part in a message board discussion concerning many different topics. Be sure to read the feature articles, too.

Library of Congress — American Memory

http://rs6.loc.gov/amhome.html

The Library of Congress American Memory Collection is one of the premiere sites on the Web. Would you like to see the Gettysburg Address? Would you like to hear Theodore Roosevelt? At this site you will find entire books, historical pictures, primary documents, recordings, movie clips, and much more. You can find information by date, place, subject category, Library Division, etc. Prepare to be overwhelmed—but in the best sense of the word.

Links to the Past: Explore America's Past

http://www.cr.nps.gov/colherit.htm

Discover the many cultural aspects of the United States at this National Park Service site. You can learn about archeological sites, buildings, landscaping, people, and events.

Mayan Culture

http://www.kstrom.net/isk/maya/mayastor.html

At this Mayan cultural site, you can read traditional storyteller's tales (rabbit stories, cautionary tales, skunk and the rabbit, etc.) and about Maya village life today. If you are adventurous, learn the pronunciations of words, phrases, and numbers.

Meeting of Frontiers

http://frontiers.loc.gov/

If you want to compare the Russian expansion through Siberia to the American expansion through the western frontier, then this is the place. While most people believe there are many differences between these two countries, there are surprising similarities that are evident at this site.

Mr. Dowling's Electronic Passport

http://www.mrdowling.com/index.html

This is an incredible history and geography site. The diverse topics include: Conflicts in the Middle East, India to the Himalayas, Chinese History, Russia and Communism, Canada, Mexico and Central America, and more.

My History is America's History

http://www.myhistory.org/

This site is a gathering place for the millions of Americans whose family stories make up our national heritage, and a starting point for those who want to learn more about their own history and the history we all share. Discover more about your ancestors' time and place in history, post a story online, search for your family online, or create a family tree.

Mummies Unwrapped

http://library.thinkquest.org/J003409/

When people think of mummies, they usually think of Egyptian variety. But there are many other types of mummies, some of which are formed through natural circumstances. This site explores the many types of mummies and where they have been found. Don't miss the additional activities!

Palos East Pow Wow

http://www.ash.udel.edu/incoming/east2/namerican/powweb.html

Imagine that you were asked to help The Field Museum expand the Native American exhibit by studying Native American tribes. Based upon research, you will design and present an exhibit displaying various aspects of the tribes' life in the Palos East museum. Sound like fun? Although this originated as a group activity, you can do this solo. Good resources accompany this site.

Pony Express Home Station

http://www.xphomestation.com/

Ranked among the most remarkable feats to come out of the 1860 American West, the Pony Express was in service from April 1860 to November 1861. Its primary mission was to deliver mail and news between St. Joseph, Missouri, and San Francisco, California.

Remember the Alamo

http://www.esc20.net/etprojects/formats/sampler/misc99/alamos/alamos.htm

'Remember the Alamo' was the cry of many Mexican rebels at the battle of San Jacinto. Have you ever wondered what really happened at the Alamo and why people were so outraged? This is the place to find the answers. In this subject sampler you will learn many new and interesting things about the Alamo using various websites from the World Wide Web.

The Revolutionary War: A Journey Towards Freedom

http://library.thinkquest.org/10966/

For anyone interested in American history, this is a great resource covering the American Revolution. An illustrated tour of Valley Forge and Washington's Crossing provides pictures and explanations of these famous places. The extensive document collection includes speeches, letters, and other important papers of the times. The biographical section has an extensive list of key historical figures, and the Forum is an area to post questions. Also, the site's games make learning fun.

Shawnee Scavenger Hunt

http://www.plainfield.k12.in.us/hschool/webq/webq29/shawnee.htm

Indiana, which means "Land of the Indians," was once home to the Shawnee Indians. This scavenger hunt will introduce you to the Shawnee and, hopefully, stimulate your curiosity to learn more about them. The site was developed for junior high use.

Sights and Sounds

http://www.codetalk.fed.us/planet/sights.html

This site showcases art and music of Native Americans. See the artwork of Mexican American school children, listen to the music of folk singers and various groups, and watch multimedia productions.

Stamps on Black History

http://library.thinkquest.org/2667/

In 1940, Booker T. Washington became the first black American to be pictured on a U.S. postage stamp. Since then, many other black Americans have been so honored. There is a complete listing of those stamps illustrated at this excellent site. From Percy Lavon Julian, a scientist in the field of medical research, to the bandleader Count Basie, you'll find the biographies of a number of these outstanding Americans.

Themes and Cultures

http://www.metmuseum.org/explore/themes.asp

Explore in-depth features on select Met galleries, past exhibitions, and a variety of other topics. Some of the past and current features include Flowers Underfoot, Indian Carpets of the Mughal Era, The Glory of Byzantium, and The New Greek Galleries. Check back often for newly added topics.

Those Were the Days

http://www.440.com/twtd/today.html

Find out what happened on this day in history by visiting "Those were the Days." Learn about what happened on the current day through events, birthdays, and chart toppers (music). This site has an archive so you are able to review any other day as well.

Through the Eyes of an Artist: Learning About America in the 1800s

http://www.ultranet.com/~schene/whomer.html

Here you can go on a journey and keep a journal of your visual, literary, and informational experiences. You will visit various parts of the United States and discover different aspects of life in the 1800s through the paintings of the great American artist, Winslow Homer. A keen observer, Mr. Homer lived for a time in the Adirondacks, which were often the subject of his paintings.

Vikings

http://www.mnh.si.edu/vikings/start.html

At this Smithsonian site you will be able to find out about the influence of the Vikings on North America and see a map that traces the voyage of the Vikings.

Why a Panama Canal?

http://www.ash.udel.edu/incoming/mhall/

Do you know why the Panama Canal was built? Find out what the students of Glasgow High School learned about the Panama Canal. At this site you will learn about their insights and read their reflections on this project.

Zoom Explorers

http://www.enchantedlearning.com/explorers/

Here is a site that is a great starting point for learning about explorers. There are three ways to go about finding information: alphabetically, by region, or by time period. You can even make a request by email for information on any explorer that isn't listed.

History
Famous People in History

75 Suffragists

http://www.inform.umd.edu/EdRes/Topic/WomensStudies/Readin
gRoom/History/Vote/75-suffragists.html

Who were the women involved in the suffragist movement, the force that obtained the vote for American women? This site gives an overview of 75 of the women who made an impact at this significant time in history. Notables like Jane Adams and Elizabeth Cady Stanton are included.

Biography.com

http://www.biography.com/

Your opportunity to get personal with over 15,000 notable figures and celebrities! With biographies for people from Roas Parks to Jimmy Hoffa, you're sure to find information for that school report here.

Meet Amazing Americans

http://www.americaslibrary.gov/cgi-bin/page.cgi/aa

When needing to do a quick study on an American figure, you should look here. This site is a great biographical overview on some amazing Americans. Some of the figures covered include Duke Ellington, Buffalo Bill Cody, and Theodore Roosevelt.

Women in American History

http://women.eb.com/

The field of women's history has begun to transform the way the overall history of the United States has been told. This site from Encyclopedia Britannica brings you all kinds of information about the women that shaped our country.

Napoleon Boneparte

http://www.lucidcafe.com/library/95aug/napoleon.html

This site gives a short overview of this astounding character. If you are seeking more information, you can scroll down on the screen and find many links that will lead you to more complete information on this historical figure.

Thomas Alva Edison

http://www.si.edu/lemelson/edison/html/his_life.html

Thomas Edison, the quintessential inventor, (e.g., phonograph, the light bulb and the telephone transmitter,) was born in Ohio and then moved to Michigan, New York, and New Jersey. This site gives background information about this unique man's life and his many, many inventions.

Ben Franklin: Glimpses of the Man

http://sln.fi.edu/franklin/rotten.html

"If you would not be forgotten as soon as you are dead and forgotten, either write things worth reading or do things worth the writing." B. Franklin. America has never forgotten Benjamin Franklin because he did both. He lived these words of wisdom by writing as much as he possibly could and by doing even more. He became famous for being a scientist, inventor, statesman, printer, philosopher, musician, and an economist. A visit to this site will give the viewer insights on this great man.

The Man - The Mahatma (Mahatma Gandhi)

http://library.thinkquest.org/26523/

The Mahatma, as Gandhi is often called, brought a great deal of peace to India as he helped free the country from British rule. Additionally he is known as a great statesman, philosopher and spiritual leader. Visit this site to gain more information about this great man.

John Hanson...Their Stamp on History

http://www.stamponhistory.com/people/hanson.html

Learn about John Hanson, the first president of the United States under the Articles of Confederation, and see the U.S. Postal stamp in honor of this often forgotten man. Links provide additional information on this man, and also on George Washington, the first official president of the United States.

Thomas Jefferson

http://www.americaslibrary.gov/pages/jb_0413_jefferso_1.html

Jefferson was a man of many talents—artist, architect, legislator, scientist, writer, diplomat, President of the United States, and more. Discover more about this man and his many accomplishments.

Martin Luther King Jr.

http://www.kidlink.org:80/KIDPROJ/dream99/

Through this site, students around the world will be writing a collaborative poem, titled "I Have a Dream," in honor of Martin Luther King's birthday. Kids are invited to take part in this interactive, poetry-writing project.

Lewis and Clark: The Journey of the Core of Discovery

http://www.pbs.org/lewisandclark/index.html

This website on Lewis and Clark was created in collaboration with the Ken Burn's PBS broadcast of the same name. At the site, you will learn about the travels of this famous duo and the people who accompanied them on their incredible journey.

Abraham Lincoln Online

http://www.netins.net/showcase/creative/lincoln.html

Abraham Lincoln, the 16th president of the United States, is a well-loved, American hero. This site includes historic Lincoln sites, speeches and writings, news and events, an index to Lincoln links, a Lincoln quiz, and resources and pictures.

Forbidden Territory - David Livingston

http://www.nationalgeographic.com/features/97/lantern/

This site tells the story of the unique figure, Dr. Livingston, a missionary from Scotland who traveled across the continent of Africa. His writings about his travels to the "Dark Continent" were enlightening to the world.

Samual F. B. Morse

http://www.invent.org/book/book-text/76.html

This site gives a brief overview of Samual Morse and his invention—Morse Code—that helped change the world. Click on the RA symbol and you will be able to listen to the Inventor Minute about Mr. Morse. (Requires Real Audio.)

Betsy Ross Homepage

http://www.ushistory.org/betsy/

Betsy Ross, the woman who sewed the first American flag, is an American hero. Read all about Betsy, learn about the American flag (including flag etiquette), and take a virtual tour of Betsy's house in Philadelphia.

Harriet Tubman and the Underground Railroad

http://www2.lhric.org/pocantico/tubman/tubman.html

This site, put together by a second grade class and teacher, has a wealth of information about Harriet Tubman and the Underground Railroad. Read character sketches and poems, and take a quiz.

George Washington

http://www.americaslibrary.gov/cgi-bin/page.cgi/aa

Come to this site, click on the George Washington link, and read about George's birthday. He was born 20 years before the introduction of the calendar used today. Find out at this site how his birthday was discovered.

Eli Whitney's Patent for the Cotton Gin

http://www.nara.gov/education/cc/whitney.html

Eli Whitney had a patent on his invention, the Cotton Gin. Read about the turmoil he had to go through until the copyright laws changed and more effectively protected his invention against copies of his machines.

Wright Brothers Aeroplane Company and Museum of Pioneer Aviation

http://www.wright-brothers.org/

This incredible site highlights the Wright Brothers, their first flight, and the history of aviation. Almost every link connects to wonderful pictures and sketches. Check out the links for the kite and various planes used in the brothers' experiments.

Holidays
General

Celebrate Holidays in the U.S.A.

http://www.usis.usemb.se/Holidays/celebrate/index.html

Did you know that the days the President of the United States designates as holidays do not have to be observed in all the 50 states? Each state can make its own holidays (yet they mostly follow the lead of the federal government). Find out much more about the National holidays celebrated in the United States and some of the other holidays that are religious or just fun.

Holiday Page

http://wilstar.com/holidays/index.html

Would you like to know the meaning of a holiday or the number of days to the holiday? You can get all of that information here. Click on the holiday and you will find plenty of information and links to other related sites.

Holidays and Events

http://features.learningkingdom.com/holiday/

Learn what happened on this day by visiting the Holidays and Events site. Several events are listed for each day along with relevant links when available. Don't miss a day—subscribe to this site. Appropriate for grades 7+.

Holidays Around the World for K-12

http://falcon.jmu.edu/%7Eramseyil/holidays.htm

This site has an incredible number of links that have to do with Holidays. They include: April Fools Day, Armistice Day, Chinese New Year, Christmas, Columbus Day, Earth Day, Flag Day, Kwanzaa, Labor Day, Martin Luther King, Jr. Day, Presidents' Day, and Valentine's Day.

Holidays
January

Happy New Year from PrimaryGames.com

http://www.primarygames.com/holidays/new_years/new_years.htm

Print and color New Year's pages, make a new calendar, count down to the New Year, and write resolutions. Even send New Year's postcards to friends and family!

Merpy's New Year Celebration

http://www.merpy.com/newyear/

Choose a language and this site will tell you how to say "Happy New Year" in that language. Maybe it'll come in handy next year!

Happy Birthday Martin Luther King, Jr.

http://www.geocities.com/Athens/Acropolis/1465/mlk.html

Find out more about the courageous man at this website created in his honor. Enjoy reading the poems written about him, and explore the content of this user friendly site.

Chinese New Year

http://jasono.hypermart.net/main.htm

If you are not Chinese, you may not know much about the Chinese New Year. You will after you visit this site! Just click on "enter here" to find the following information and more: When Is the Chinese New Year?, the Origin of the Chinese New Year, Traditions of the Chinese New Year, and a photo gallery.

Holidays
February

Groundhog Day

http://www.gojp.com/groundhog/

Find out about Punxsutawney Phil, our favorite groundhog, and see how many more days of winter we will have. There is a shadow report available at this site along with plenty of information. Other Groundhog links are available at this site.

Official Site of the Punxsutawney Groundhog Club

http://www.groundhog.org/

Everything you wanted to know about the groundhog and the history of the day. Features Quicktime VR movies, Groundhog Club information, predictions, and a fun game!

Abraham Lincoln

http://www.siec.k12.in.us/~west/proj/lincoln/

Read about the famous President, view pictures, and try the treasure hunt. A teacher and her students created this site. It's especially enjoyable for kids in the early grades.

George Washington

http://www.history.org/people/washhdr.htm

This site includes information on the first president, including his biography, inaugural addresses, writings, and more. Particularly interesting: an excerpt from a children's book based on George Washington's own diary and a piece from an etiquette book transcribed by George Washington when he was a kid.

Holidays
February

The Activity Idea Place: Valentine's Day

http://www.123child.com/val/

Want activity ideas for young kids? Try this site where you will find art and craft ideas, songs, book recommendations, games, and much more. If you are creating a Valentine's Day web page, there are interesting backgrounds and borders available.

History Channel - History of Valentine's Day

http://www.historychannel.com/exhibits/valentine/

Every February, across the country, candy, flowers, and gifts are exchanged between loved ones, all in the name of St. Valentine. But who is this mysterious saint and why do we celebrate this holiday? Find out at this site!

The Love Calculator

http://www.lovecalculator.com/

What's in a name? This site designed by Doctor Love calculates the probability of a successful relationship between two people based on just one thing: their names!

Love Letters

http://www.usps.gov/letters/volume2/love-main.html

Need a little inspiration for your Valentine's love letters? This U.S. Postal Service site shows you letters by Heloise, King Henry VIII, Napoleon, Lord Byron, and others throughout history. How romantic!

Holidays
March

Pi Day

http://planetpi.8m.com/

It's not widely celebrated, but Pi Day is a special day when the great number of pi is celebrated. It is usually on March 14 because pi's first three digits are 3.14. Find out what Pi is, the history of Pi, the uses of Pi, and even Pi pics and songs!

History Channel - History of St. Patrick's Day

http://www.historychannel.com/exhibits/stpatricksday/main.html

St. Patrick, the patron saint of Ireland, is one of Christianity's most widely known figures. But for all his celebrity, his life remains somewhat of a mystery. Many of the stories traditionally associated with St. Patrick, including the famous account of his banishing all the snakes from Ireland, are false, the products of hundreds of years of exaggerated storytelling. This site gives you the real scoop.

Lucky Leprechaun's Lane

http://www.usacitylink.com/citylink/lucky/

This netland of magical mists, lucky leprechauns, and lots of green has plenty of fun things to do, explore, celebrate, and learn. This site features activities celebrating March 17 and the great country of Ireland.

St. Patrick's Day

http://www.st-patricks-day.com/

So who exactly was St. Patrick? And what does the shamrock have to do with St. Patrick's Day? This site attempts to enlighten and entertain as it steps back in time to explore the legend of St. Patrick.

Holidays
April

---

13 Great April Fools' Pranks

http://family.go.com/Features/family_1999_03/famf/famf39pranks/

Have some fun on April Fool's Day with some fun-loving pranks. For instance, learn how to make pretend spilled coffee or a fake doughnut. Give your parents a thrill when you complain about the dandruff you have. You find these jokes and more at this site.

Kids Domain Easter Time

http://www.kidsdomain.com/holiday/easter/

This site will help you spring into your Easter celebration! Adopt a chick, play some Easter games, color fun pictures, send an e-card, read online stories, and lots more.

Planetpals: About Earth Day

http://www.planetpals.com/earthday.html

Don't forget to celebrate Earth Day on April 22nd—this site can help. Read quick Earth Day recycling and reusing tips and tricks, see what various classes are doing to celebrate, send an email sticker to a friend, and lots more!

National Arbor Day Foundation

http://www.arborday.org/

Did you know that Arbor Day is a nationally celebrated observance that encourages tree planting and tree care? Founded by J. Sterling Morton in Nebraska in 1872, National Arbor Day is celebrated each on the last Friday in April. This site give the history of this day and even tells how you can get free trees to plant in honor of this day.

Holidays
May

May Day

http://www.umkc.edu/imc/mayday.htm

May Day is a festival of happiness, joy and the coming of summer. This site is designed to help teacher's celebrate the holiday, but is a good source for May Day facts and fun.

Cinco de Mayo

http://www.noblenet.org/year/tty5cin.htm

This site has all kinds of links to Cinco de Mayo sites. You will find crafts, art projects, recipes, electronic greetings, and lots of information.

Happy Mother's Day

http://www.kidsdomain.com/holiday/

If Mother's Day is coming, you must visit this site. (Click on Mother's Day on the Holiday page.) You can send an electronic card or craft a card. You will find ideas for gifts you can make. Would you like to read a book about Mother's Day? There are book suggestions and much more.

Memorial Day

http://wilstar.com/holidays/memday.htm

Memorial Day is celebrated every May, but do you really understand what this holiday is all about? This site provides background information on this day that we celebrate the men and women who have died in service to our country.

Holidays
June & July

The Unofficial American Flag Home Page!

http://www.auburn.edu/~herndmm/flag.htm

Celebrate Flag Day on June 14th at this site—everything you want to know about the American Flag is probably here. For instance, you can find the words to "You're a Grand Old Flag" and photos of the flag. Be sure to click on "The Best American Flag Related Links."

Father's Day

http://www.kidsdomain.com/holiday/

As you prepare for Father's Day, visit this site. (Click on Father's Day on the Holiday page.) You will find all you need here. Want to send an electronic card or make your own? The links are here for either one. You can also find puzzles and games on this topic. If you want to make a gift, there are plenty of ideas available.

Kid's Domain July 4th Fun!

http://www.kidsdomain.com/holiday

If you need to get into the 4th of July spirit, visit this site. (Click on July 4th on the Holiday page.) You will find information on the holiday and why it is celebrated. Additionally, there are games, word searches, e-cards, activities and crafts, and even holiday software for Macs and PCs.

Marvelicious Independence Day

http://www.marvelicious.com/independence.html

This site has everything from picnic games to information about what happened to the 56 men who signed the Declaration of Independence. Also includes links to tons of other 4th of July sites.

Holidays
August & September

The Friendship Page

http://www.friendship.com.au/friendday.html

You may not know it, but International Friendship Day is on August 1st. This site has suggestions on how to celebrate your friends—from posting a tribute on the Web to making a friendship bracelet.

Labor Day

http://wilstar.com/holidays/

This site provides information on Labor Day, the day that we celebrate all the workers of the United States and all that they contribute to the country. This holiday is also celebrated in Canada and other countries. (From the Holiday page, scroll down to the Labor Day link.)

National Grandparents Day

http://www.grandparents-day.com/

Learn how Grandparents Day began, and find out all about this holiday in honor of grandmas and grandpas. You can even check out artwork, essays, and poetry other kids have written about their grandparents!

Virtual Jerusalem Days of Awe Site

http://www.vjholidays.com/rosh/kids.htm

Learn all about the customs of Rosh Hashanah and Yom Kippur at this site. Click around in the Game Zone, listen to some great tales in Storyland, and make lots of exciting things in the Arts & Crafts Center.

Holidays
October

Columbus Navigation Homepage

http://www1.minn.net/~keithp

Learn about Columbus through this site. There is information on Columbus' four voyages to the New World, his ships, crew, and much more. Try the links to other helpful sites.

Columbus Day

http://www.geocities.com/Athens/Acropolis/1465/columbus.html

This is a delightful site about the explorer Christopher Columbus. Click on the "Columbus Day for Children" link for some activities. Other links include books, timeline, and voyages.

Ben & Jerry's Halloween

http://www.benjerry.com/halloween

Have some Halloween fun at Ben & Jerry's site. Enter the Haunted House where you can see all of the Ben & Jerry flavors that have been retired—well, maybe not if you vote to get them back. Also, watch the Halloween iMovie and try the links for craft activities, coloring book, and more.

Dia de Los Muertos

http://www.azcentral.com/rep/dead/

This colorful, informative site gives a history of the day. It talks about the history, food, events, culture, and more of this Mexican holiday. Includes a glossary, videos, photos, and timeline.

Holidays
October

Goosebumps Goulish Gathering

http://www.foxhome.com/goosebumps/gatmain.html

Plan a goulish gathering with help from Goosebumps. Follow the tips on this site and you'll create a nightmare your friends will never forget. There are décor ideas to turn your home into a house of horrors, fiendishly fun activities, scary souvenirs, terror-ific treat ideas, and more.

HalloweenMagazine.com

http://www.halloweenmagazine.com/

This family-friendly site contains links to all kinds of Halloween content, including activities, articles, stories, history, recipes, downloads, and decoration ideas. You can easily link to places to buy costumes, wigs, accessories, and props. And, all trick-or-treaters should take the safety quiz.

Haunted Home Page

http://www.hauntedhome.com/

Enter the Haunted Home Page if you dare… This site's main attraction is an interactive game where you can explore a haunted house filled with monsters and mayhem, secret passages, trap doors, and other appalling perils. Other items found here: trick-or-treating safety tips, pumpkin-carving stencils/patterns, spooky sound files, and a cyberbook of eerie Halloween lore.

Hershey's Halloween

http://www.hersheys.com/trickortreats/fun.html

Here, you can try out a few pumpkin-carving ideas on a virtual pumpkin before carving the real thing. Get in the Halloween spirit with spooky screensavers and creepy wallpaper. Plus, find out secrets for creating the perfect Jack-O-Lantern and use free stencils to carve your next design!

Holidays
November

Sadie Hawkins Day

http://www.lil-abner.com/sadiehawk.html

Sadie Hawkins Day, an American folk event, made its debut in Al Capp's Li'l Abner strip November 15, 1937. Find out the history behind this day where girls ask out boys.

Celebrate! Holidays in the U.S.A.: Veterans' Day

http://www.usis.usemb.se/Holidays

Scroll down to Veteran's Day to get some historical background on this special American holiday. Find out why this holiday's name was changed from Armistice to Vererans' Day.

An American Thanksgiving

http://www.night.net/thanksgiving/

This site contains information on the First Thanksgiving and the way that it is celebrated in America. Click on Fun Activities and you will find poems, stories, activities, craft projects and more. The "And More" link will take you to other sites.

Mayflower Web Pages

http://members.aol.com/calebj/mayflower.html

Learn about the Pilgrims and their struggles to come to America. This site offers information on the Mayflower, the crew, passenger list, and even their inventory. There are links to doctrines from the Mayflower, passenger wills, etc. Be sure you scroll down to Historical Information.

Holidays
December

History Channel - History of the Holidays

http://www.historychannel.com/exhibits/holidays/main.html

Learn about the real traditions and stories behind Christmas, Hanukkah, and Kwanzaa at this informational site. Lots of interesting and well-written tidbits that are great for clearing up myths and getting the facts!

Happy Chanukah!

http://www.kidsdomain.com/holiday

Chanukah, or the Festival of Lights, is presented at this site. Click on the Menorah to learn about this Jewish holiday, play games, or download related software for either the Mac or a PC. If you are creating a webpage, there is a clip art page that contains art and plenty of other links to art.

World Wide Jewish Web Chanuka.com

http://www.chanuka.com/

Visit this site to get a taste of Chanuka. There is much to explore at this informative site. Links include menorah, dreidels, calendar, history, and recipes. Even if you are not Jewish, come to this site and send a Chanuka postcard to a friend.

Afro-Americ@: Kwanzaa

http://www.afroam.org/children/fun/kwanzaa/kwanzaa.html

This site is designed just for kids and helps them learn the history of the holiday and the seven principles. Includes lots of help pronouncing Kwanzaa words and easy, short explanations.

Holidays
December

Kid's Kourt Happy Kwanzaa

http://www.kidskourt.com/Holidays/KwanPage.htm

This site offers the history of the celebration, coloring pages, desktop themes, clip art, and other activities. There are a lot of words to read on this site, but it's very informative for older kids.

Christmas.com Fun & Entertainment!

http://christmas.com/fun/

This site greets kids with a countdown to Christmas. It includes online games, a Christmas coloring book, proof that Santa exists, and holiday cursors and desktop themes. You can even join the EIB (Elves in Black), the first, last, and only organization dedicated to preserving the Spirit of Christmas.

Christmas! Christmas! Christmas! Not Just for Kids!

http://www.night.net/christmas/

If Christmas is your holiday, then visit this site. There is music playing when you reach the home page to get you in the Christmas spirit (requires MIDI). You can choose links such as: Santa Claus, Christmas Stories and Poems, Feasting for the Christmas Season, and more.

Germanic Christmas Links

http://www.german-way.com/german/christmas2.html

This site in German and English provides information on the Christmas customs of Germany. There are many, many links below the first frame of links. Be aware that some of the links go inactive after the holidays until the following season when they restart.

Holidays
December

Merry-Christmas.com

http://www.merry-christmas.com/

This homepage for the Christmas season includes games, activities, and coloring for kids. You can find holiday music, printable gift tags, ornament craft ideas, histories of Christmas tree and Santa Claus, and more.

North-Pole.net

http://www.north-pole.net/

This charming site, which claims to be Santa's official website, can be viewed in English, German, Spanish, French, and Portuguese. One of the best features of this site is the free email address that can be used during the holidays—it says yourname@north-pole.net.

Official North Pole

http://www.officialnorthpole.com/

At this site you can e-mail Santa, view the naughty or nice list, play some reindeer games, and more! We like the Santa Tracker, which tells you how close Santa is to your house (and how many cookies he's eaten!).

Online Christmas Songbook

http://rememberjosie.org/carols/

All of the music on this page is provided so that you can get out with your friends and family and sing. Print these pages freely. The song list is quite extensive; you will sing for days!

Kids Clubs & Organizations

4-H

http://www.4-H.org

4-H is the youth education branch of the Cooperative Extension Service, a program of the United States Department of Agriculture. Each state and each county has access to a County Extension office for both youth and adult programs. Click on Resources for interesting links.

Boys and Girls Clubs of America

http://www.bgca.org

Boys and Girls Clubs are a safe place to learn and grow—all while having fun. Club programs and services promote and enhance the development of boys and girls by instilling a sense of competence, usefulness, belonging and influence. Visit this site to find out more.

Boy Scouts of America

http://www.bsa.scouting.org

This website is about the Boy Scout of America—Tiger Cubs, Cub Scouting, Boy Scouting, and Venturing. You can sign up for scouting at this site or find helpful information about its 300 local councils.

CampFire Boys and Girls

http://www.campfire.org/campfire_nf.html

CampFire Boys and Girls clubs are for children of all ages! Boys and girls nationwide participate in fun activities, projects, events, and lots of other activities that come with a small group experience. This site is a great resource for member of this organization and those who might be considering membership.

Girl Scouts of the USA

http://www.gsusa.org/

This helpful site contains the latest news about the organization, troops, girls, and more. Girl Scouts will want to visit the Just for Girls area where they can chat, ask questions, get information on badges, and much more.

Little League Online

http://www.littleleague.org/

Get the latest Little League news, learn to start a new league, read about Little League structure and divisions, find a local league, and more. Plus, there's fun stuff like a Little League photo contest and coverage on the year's Little League World Series.

YMCA

http://www.ymca.net

Do you know what Martin Luther King Jr., Susan Sarandon, and John Glen have in common? When they were kids they all were involved with the YMCA. This site provides information on local chapters, their newsletters online, and much more.

YWCA

http://www.ywca.org/

Learn about the YWCA, an organization for women, at this site. In addition to their calendar of events, you will find local chapter information, news, and other organization information.

Math

A+ Math

http://www.aplusmath.com/

This website was developed to help students improve their math skills interactively. Visit the game room and play exciting games like Matho and Hidden Picture. Create and print your own set of flashcards online, try the Homework Helper to check your homework solutions, and more.

AAA Math

http://www.aaamath.com

This site contains hundreds of pages of Basic Math Skills that are divided by grade level or by topic. Each page has interactive practice, an explanation of the math topic, and several challenge games. The math problems are randomly created, so you'll never run out!

Absurd Math

http://www.hrmvideo.com/abmath

This site is an interactive pre-algebra problem solving game series. The player proceeds on missions in a strange world where the ultimate power consists of mathematical skill and knowledge. Many of the pages have hidden clues and areas.

Algebra Online

http://www.algebra-online.com

Need help with Algebra? Try this site! Look at the questions posted on the MathBoard to see if your question has already been answered. If not, pose your problem in the Personal Help section. Note their requirements and the 24-48 hour turn-around time.

Algebra Modules/Lessons

http://www.purplemath.com/modules/modules.htm

Okay, all of you high achievers, here is a site for you. This site will help you get to the head of the Algebra class. You will find lessons and, more importantly, good explanations that can guide you to new understandings.

AllMath.com

http://www.allmath.com/

This site is full of math stuff, including math flashcards, multiplication tables, biographies of mathematicians, and a glossary of math terms.

Ask Dr. Math

http://forum.swarthmore.edu/dr.math/dr-math.html

Ask Dr. Math is the place to go if you want an answer to a math question. With more than 300 mathematicians ready to answer questions, you're sure to get a reply! Send in request via their online web form. The best questions are archived by grade level and topics.

BrainBashers

http://www.brainbashers.com/

This unique collection of brain teasers, games, and optical illusions is updated with at least 5 new puzzles each Sunday. You can select brain teasers, word puzzles, and math puzzles to perplex your mind. You can also select one of the games to wile away the hours, or perhaps an illusion to befuddle the eyes.

Brain Teasers

http://www.eduplace.com/math/brain/index.html

Every Wednesday kids will find a new brain teaser at this site. The teasers are for grades 3-5, 5 & 6, and 7 & up. You will have to wait for the answer—it is posted the following week along with a new challenge for the week. An archive of past teasers is available.

Clocks and Time

http://www.ubr.com/clocks

This humble site contains lots of information about clocks and time. Click on Education and find out how a pendulum clock works or see inside an alarm clock. You will find clock museums, learn about sundials, and much more.

Coolmath.com

http://www.coolmath.com

Explore this amusement park of mathematics! Have fun with interactive activities and games like Lemonade Stand and Arithmattack. There's stuff for parents and teachers, too.

DiscoverySchool.com Math

http://school.discovery.com/students/math.html

Mom and Dad stumped? The problem solvers on this site will explain your math homework with step-by-step instructions (and the answers, too). Plus, tease your brain with an archive of mind-boggling logic puzzles.

Elementary Problem of the Week (Grades 3-6)

http://forum.swarthmore.edu/elempow/

Take part in this exciting Mathematics group. The Math Forum will pose a problem and you (with a small team of 4 or an entire class) can contribute to the solution. Be sure to read their Information and Guidelines section.

Figure This! Math Challenges for Families

http://www.figurethis.org/

Math can be fun when you involve the whole family! Challenge your siblings and parents with these stumpers. New brainteasers posted every week. Check out "How to Use This Site" for more information on software required.

Geometry of the Ancients

http://www.learningwave.com/engage/geometry/geometry.html

This exploration into area, perimeter, and volume includes practice sheets of geometry basics and critical thinking application activities. Visit the "Challenge of the 7 Cups" and solve the geometry riddles of the Gate of Janus.

Harcourt Math Advantage

http://www.hbschool.com/menus/math_advantage.html

Choose your grade and get games and problems specifically targeted for kids at your level. Don't forget to check the multimedia math glossary, a great reference for math terms and definitions!

Numeracy Resources

http://www.numeracyresources.co.uk

This site offers five interactive math games: Archimedes in his Bath, Transformation Golf, Splat! (angle estimation), Post the Shapes, and Fraction Pairs. Visit the subscription site, Maths Online (http://www.mathsonline.co.uk/), for even more games, puzzles, activities, and worksheets.

Macalester College Problem of the Week

http://forum.swarthmore.edu/wagon/

Join this Problem of the Week mailing list to receive a mathematical challenge. Be aware that the problems can be challenging, but the answers are available online. Appropriate for grades 10+.

Math Cats

http://www.mathcats.com

The first thing you see when you get to this site is a math problem on the Magic Chalkboard. Click the cat to enter the site and find MicroWorlds projects and interesting, exploratory activities, like Tessellation Town and Exploding Math Art.

MathDork

http://www.mathdork.com

This pre-algebra and algebra site is a subscription service with a mission of providing an interactive learning environment that compliments the student's everyday curriculum. Try the free sample lessons to get a sense of what the site has to offer before you subscribe.

Math for Morons Like Us

http://library.thinkquest.org/20991/home.html

Do you need some extra help with math? If so, you will find this site to be very helpful. The topics included here range from pre-algebra to calculus. Additionally, you will find tutorials, sample problems, and quizzes. There is a discussion board for you to find quick help—calculus students have their own discussion board—and there is a formula database should you need one.

Math in Daily Life

http://www.learner.org/exhibits/dailymath/

At this site, you'll look at math principles through common situations, such as playing games or cooking. The situations are geared toward adults (home decorating, buying a car, etc.), but there are plenty of concrete concepts here that teens can appreciate.

MathMastery.com

http://www.mathmastery.com

This great looking site is dedicated to helping students practice and understand essential math skills. DailyBrains are original thematic math problems created by teachers, and the CyberChallenge provides students with a timed setting for practicing math facts in addition, subtraction, multiplication, and division. In addition, you can sign up for MyMathClass, a subscription-based curriculum program for students in the 3rd through 8th grades.

Megamaths

http://www.bbc.co.uk/education/megamaths/

This British site has problem solving areas for kids ages 7-9. They can practice multiplication in the World of Tables or shape properties in the World of Shapes.

Middle School Problem of the Week (Grades 7 & 8)

http://forum.swarthmore.edu/midpow/

Have the fun of exploring mathematics with peers outside of your class and school. As you solve the problems posed by the Math forum, you will work with an online community. Check out the Information and Guidelines section for background information.

Mrs. Glosser's Math Goodies

http://www.mathgoodies.com/

Math Goodies is a free educational website featuring interactive math lessons, homework help, worksheets, puzzles, message boards, and more! The site has over 400 pages of free math activities and resources for students, teachers, and parents, including problems on geometry, percentages, factoring, and more.

Multiplication.com

http://www.multiplication.com/

Multiply your math knowledge with this site full of math games, worksheets, flashcards, and quizzes. Plenty of teacher-designed that can help you memorize the times tables.

Online Math Applications

http://tqjunior.advanced.org/4116/

This site teaches kids of all ages a simple and interesting approach to math that applies to real world situations. It also includes a simulated stock market game.

Preschool Math

http://www.familyplay.com/activities/actPremath.html

Try this site for some introductory math activities to play with a preschool child.
You will find activities that use basic household items and cover subjects such as
categorizing, measuring, matching, and patterning.

PrimaryGames.com Math

http://www.primarygames.com/math.htm

This site for young kids includes math games, flashcard activities, math stories,
shape practice, time-telling games, addition drills, and more.

ThePuzzleFactory.com

http://www.thepuzzlefactory.com

Find online jigsaw puzzles, slider puzzles, word puzzles, tangrams, and more.
Even become a member and receive the latest puzzle and game info by email.

Puzzlemaker

http://puzzlemaker.school.discovery.com/

Puzzlemaker is a puzzle generation tool for teachers, students, and parents. Create
and print customized word search, crossword, or math puzzles. Build your own
maze or print hand-drawn mazes created around holidays and classroom topics.

Money & Finance

Escape from Knab

http://www.escapefromknab.com/

Escape from Knab is an educational simulation which takes participants through a series of financial decision-making experiences in the fun and entertaining setting of the fictitious planet, Knab. The basic goal of the site is to develop background knowledge in preparation for real-life financial situations.

FleetKids

http://www.fleetkids.com

FleetKids is all about encouraging learning through inquiry and getting kids started out on the path to money smarts. The activities on the site reflect real-world money experiences—kids can play a stock market game, manage a baseball team, set up a business plan, and more. Schools can sign up for the program and compete to win prizes.

H.I.P. Pocket Change

http://www.usmint.gov/kids/

Do you have any idea what's jangling around in your pockets? If you said nickels and dimes, you don't know the half of it. There's more awesome history in coins than even in your principal's head! Kids, knock on the Clubhouse door and join others who flip for coins.

Kids Can Save

http://www.kidscansave.gc.ca/E1-splash.htm

Some people think that the earlier kids learn about money, the better. This site is a good starting place. Kids can play The Snossel of Toog game to get a sense about saving money and can even download a Snossel screensaver. This is a Canadian site so naturally it refers to their money system and resources, but the game is fun in any denomination!

MainXchange Stock Game

http://www.lightspan.com/kids/pages/default.asp?_prod=LS&_nav=k1

Want to learn about the Stock Market? MainXchange is the place to do a little practice trading. You need to go through the Lightspan.com site and enter into the section of MainXchange that is set aside for Lightspan users. Remember to read the disclaimers on the Lightspan.com page.

The Mint

http://www.themint.org/

Find out what it takes to start your own business, learn how to save and invest your money wisely, or try out some cool quizzes and financial tools. You can also learn about your role in the economy and how to make a budget!

Moneyopolis.com

http://www.moneyopolis.com/

Ernst & Young developed the Moneyopolis site as a public service to help kids in grades six through eight develop math and financial planning skills. While navigating through Moneyopolis, kids are encouraged to start thinking about getting an after-school job, saving for college, and setting long-term goals.

Practical Money Skills for Life

http://visa.edgate.com/visa/

This Visa-sponsored site challenges kids and young adults with fun games and contests that test their knowledge of making, managing, and using money responsibly. Includes banking terms, calculators, and fun family activities.

Royal Canadian Mint - MillenniumZone

http://www.rcmint.ca/en/millennium/kidszone/faq1.html

The MillenniumZone is nothing but games about money! There is Coin Flip, Coin Quiz, Match Game and CentSation. Read the story "The Adventures of Zachery and Penny Money."

Saving Bonds for Kids

http://www.publicdebt.treas.gov/sav/savkids.htm

The purpose of this site is to teach children about the benefits of saving at an early age, particularly with a government savings bond. Children can read about the advantages of purchasing a savings bond and how the invested money is used. A poster contest, fun facts, and games are included at this site.

The Treasury Page for Kids

http://www.treas.gov/kids/

You can begin your visit at this site by taking a virtual tour of the Treasury building. Next you can read about the history of the Treasury which includes information on the secret service, Mint history, and the history of taxes.

The Young Investor Website

http://www.younginvestor.com/pick.shtml

This site is a place to learn about investing and money. To start, you must type in a nickname, choose a button style, and pick a guide. Once inside, you'll find an online manual that teaches the basics of investing. You'll begin to understand what it means to own shares in a company, and even learn how to read a company's annual report.

Movies

Cinema - How are Hollywood Films Made?

http://www.learner.org/exhibits/cinema/

Learn about the film industry from the screenwriter to the final cut. Best of all, at this site you can actually try out the various roles of director, actor, producer, screenwriter, and editor. This is an eye-opening experience if you have ever wondered how a movie is made.

The Motion-Picture Industry: Behind the Scenes

http://library.thinkquest.org/10015/

Are you a movie fan? Have you often wondered how they make movies? Then this site is one that you should not miss. Learn all about the world of filmmaking, watch a short movie and see how it was made, and experience filmmaking with an online simulation.

The Movie Mom

http://www.moviemom.com/

Looking for a good movie to watch? Nell Minow's guide to family-friendly movies will help you find a parent-approved movie in the theaters or on video. Links to video ideas by age groups and categories.

Yahoo Movies

http://movies.yahoo.com/

Would you like to read a review on a newly released movie or one that's been around for awhile? Would you like to know where a movie is playing near you? Want to know if a movie you missed at the theater is out on video yet? You can do all that and more at the Yahoo Movie website.

Museums

American Museum of Natural History

http://www.amnh.org/

When you arrive at the museum site, you might want to make your first stop the site map because it provides a great overview of the available links. Make sure you stop by the "Just for Kids" section because of the great exhibits specifically designed for their interests.

The Bowers Kidseum

http://www.nativecreative.com/kidseum

Kidseum is more than an exhibit—it allows kids to have virtual hands-on experience with world cultures. Thematic areas are filled with treasures that can be virtually touched and played with. Listen to the sounds of Bali for a sound treat.

The British Museum

http://www.british-muscum.ac.uk/

This museum should not be missed! When you enter the site, you might want to begin with the Explore link that will launch you into different cultures. Understand will take you education and online learning. Explore will take you to an incredible site map where you will have so many wonderful choices that you will not know where to begin.

Butler Institute of American Art

http://www.butlerart.com/

Although there is extensive information about the museum if you are planning to visit, there is a small online exhibit. You will need to check back often as they change the exhibits periodically.

Carnegie Museum of Natural History

http://www.clpgh.org/cmnh/

One of the best parts of this exhibit is the Discovery Room Online, a special place for all ages to see things up close, to explore our world, and to learn something new. Exhibits include "Meet the Beetles," "Dinosaur Imposters," "Dinosaur Jumble," "Dinoscience," and many more. Also, look at the Site Map for more great exhibits.

Carnegie Science Center

http://www.carnegiesciencecenter.org/

When you arrive at the homepage at this site, click on Kids and a pop-up menu will appear. While here, try Test the G-force or Telerobot.

The Chicago Academy of Sciences Home Page

http://www.chias.org/

Visit the new Chicago Academy of Science online. If you are visiting Chicago, this site will help you plan a visit. If you can only do an online visit, click on Biology to see the exhibits. Some of the exhibits are temporary so check back often.

Children's Museum of Indianapolis

http://www.childrensmuseum.org/

The Children's Museum of Indianapolis website provides visitors with the latest information on the museum. Even if you are not a local, stop by and see the fun online activities. There are games, opportunities to learn about space, dinosaurs, and more.

Children's Museum of Manhattan

http://www.cmom.org

The Children's Museum of Manhattan (CMOM) is a not-for-profit institution, founded in 1973, to engage children and families in a partnership of learning through interactive exhibits and educational programs. CMOM inspires children and families to learn about themselves and our culturally diverse world through the arts, literacy, media and communications, science and the environment, and early childhood education.

Cité Labs

http://www.cite-sciences.fr/

This is a French web museum. When you arrive at the first screen scroll to the right to find the British flag. Clicking on this will present the site in English. Explore the site but don't miss the virtual physics lab and "Video Encyclopedia" and "Invisible World."

The Cleveland Museum of Art

http://www.clemusart.com/

This museum proudly serves dual roles as a leader in the international museum world and as a cultural and educational cornerstone of its community. Outstanding programs for scholars, artists, families, and children, as well as respected film and music series, complement the collections and a rich schedule of special exhibitions. Make sure you view the announcements of new sites because even the overview can be a wonderful lesson.

The Cleveland Museum of Natural History

http://www.cmnh.org/

The Cleveland Museum of Natural History encourages people of all ages to discover and explore the natural world. You will find information on anthropology, archaeology, astronomy, botany, geology, paleontology, zoology, and wildlife biology at this museum. Check with this site to see the schedule of exhibits.

Experimentarium

http://www.experimentarium.dk/index_uk.html

Visit this Danish museum where you will find exhibits in Danish, German, Swedish, and English. As you reach the first screen click on one of the scrolling exhibits. While you can't see the entire exhibit on line, they present enough of it for it to be a learning experience.

Exploratorium.edu

http://www.exploratorium.edu/

The mission of the Exploratorium is "to create a culture of learning through innovative environments, programs, and tools that help people to nurture their curiosity about the world around them." And this is apparent in their exhibits both at the museum and online. Some of the online exhibits include: Bird in a Cage, Changing Illusions, Shimmer, and Fading Dot.

Fine Arts Museum of San Francisco

http://www.thinker.org/

The Fine Arts Museum of San Francisco presents a spectacular art imagebase as a growing, searchable catalog of their painting, drawing, etching, sculpture, porcelain, silver, glass, furniture, and textiles collections. At this site you will find 50% of the collection from the De Young and Legion of Honor museums online, which adds up to thousands of artistic images!

Gallery of Achievement

http://www.achievement.org/

Looking for a website that could change your life? Here it is, the Gallery of Achievement. In selecting people for the Gallery of Achievers, this site focuses on individuals who have shaped the twentieth century by their accomplishments. Search for leaders through qualities like persistence, vision, or courage. How about searching for leaders in the public service, science, or art world?

Lawrence Hall of Science Kid Center

http://www.lhs.berkeley.edu/kids/

Lawrence Hall of Science has created a special website just for kids. There are separate sections for online and offline activities, and student work. While at the site you can sing, experiment, learn, and generally have a wonderful time.

Louvre

http://www.Louvre.fr

The Louvre, regarded by some as the premiere museum in the world, has its own website that offers a virtual tour of the palace and museum. A visit to the site is not complete without a look at the collection and history of the palace and museum. Choose the English version on the first screen.

The Metropolitan Museum of Art - Explore & Learn

http://www.metmuseum.org/explore/index.asp

There's plenty for older kids to explore here. They can visit the Just for Fun area for everything from discovering a dragon to exploring Korean ceramic techniques. Plus, they'll read biographies of artists, study the art history timeline, and research cultures with special features on the Met's collections and exhibitions.

Museum of Science and Industry - Chicago

http://www.msichicago.org/

This museum is fantastic to visit in person, but it is also great to visit online. Take a tour of the German U505 submarine, the Farm, the Fairly Castle, Pioneer Zephyr, or the Coal Mine. In addition, see the other exhibits that often have a minimum, but nevertheless, exciting online presence.

National Gallery of Art

http://www.nga.gov/

This site has many famous painting and artists. Take an online tour and learn about their exhibits and collections. If you are planning a vacation to Washington, D.C., this site will help you in planning a real visit to the museum.

National Gallery of Art for Kids

http://www.nga.gov/kids/kids.htm#

This site offers interesting activities and projects to help kids learn more about art. Check out the Lizzy and Gordon animated musical adventure or the art activities and projects related to a famous artist—like Kandinsky and Tissot.

Oregon Museum of Science and Industry

http://www.omsi.edu/

For a real treat, visit this website, particularly, Science Online. Once there, click on "Engineer It!" or "Innovation Station" and begin to have some fun as you learn about structures, wind, and water.

National Air and Space

http://www.nasm.edu/

This is a must-see museum when visiting in Washington D.C. You can plan your visit using the resources of this website. Additionally, you can have a great experience in just visiting this site. The online exhibit "Commemorations in the Archives" is an ever-changing online experience so check back often.

Natural History Museum of London, England

http://www.nhm.ac.uk/#

When you arrive at the home page of the Natural History Museum, go right to the Quickindex pull-down menu. Try Q.U.E.S.T. or Gobi Desert Dino or the Picture Library. If you are planning a vacation to London, this is a museum that you will want to visit. Start your planning here.

Robert C. Williams American Museum of Papermaking

http://www.ipst.edu/amp/

Take an online tour of the Paper Museum. When you arrive at the home page, click on Museum. It is recommended that you choose "Begin the Tour" on your first visit. Otherwise click away on the various sections of the museum building.

Royal British Columbia Museum

http://rbcm1.rbcm.gov.bc.ca/

If you need research data on human, modern, or natural history, you will find it here. You will also find some great pages that you can print out in PDF. Topics include: Whales, Pioneer Kitchens, Songbirds, Construction Toys, Marsh Monsters, Circus, Bats, Thunderbird Park, and Nuu-Chah-Nulth. Use the site map for a good overview.

St. Louis Science Center

http://www.slsc.org/

The St. Louis Science Center is truly a fun place. Try the Online Galleries, which includes: Cyberville, DNA Zone, Ecology & Environment Past, and Structures. When you are finished here explore the other links like Grossology.

Santa Barbara Museum of Natural History

http://www.sbnature.org/

When you visit Santa Barbara, you should visit their museum of Natural History. The comprehensive lesson, "Welcome to Chumash Indian Life" thoroughly explores this tribe of Native Americans. The Cave paintings are explained in depth right down to the color and types of paint used. You can learn about baskets, how they were made, and much more.

Science Museum of Minnesota

http://www.sci.mus.mn.us/

This is a great museum even if you are not a local. Try the "Take a Tour" and learn about the "DeadZone," or go to the "Dinosaurs and Fossils Gallery" and try to figure out the mystery object.

Science Museum of the U. K.

http://www.sciencemuseum.org.uk/on-line/frameset.htm

At the home page of this site, click on "Exhibitions Online" to find the exciting new learning opportunities from this museum. Also, try "Learn & Teach," the online activities developed for students and teachers.

Seattle Art Museum Kids Page

http://www.seattleartmuseum.org/Kids/default.htm

Create your own art exhibition online, discover the secret of porcelain, play with ancient Egyptian wigs, and learn about impressionist painting. Kids will gain art knowledge as they participate in the original activities on this site.

The State Hermitage Museum

http://www.hermitagemuseum.org

The Hermitage has over 3 million pieces of artwork from all times and people allowing them to capture the essence of the world culture. Visit here and you will have an incredible experience as you view the "Hermitage History" or the "Children & Education" site.

Virtual Smithsonian

http://2k.si.edu/

This is one of the most incredible places on the web. When you enter the Virtual Smithsonian, it tests your computer for compatibility to their website. Once you pass the test, you can take a virtual tour of this fantastic museum. If this is your first visit to this site, enter through the First Time Viewer (see pull-down menu) entrance for the computer test and instructions to make your visit spectacular.

Washingtonian Museum Guide

http://www.washingtonian.com/inwashington/museumguide/mus_kids.html

Going to Washington D.C.? Look at this site to find the best kids museum in the city. To be listed on this site, the museum has to be a real hands-on place for kids to have fun and learn.

The World of Vikings

http://www.pastforward.co.uk/vikings

This site is a clearinghouse of Viking museums. Turn to this site when you want information about their ships, sagas (Viking Lore), and more.

Music

Easy Music Theory

http://www.musictheory.halifax.ns.ca/

Would you like to learn more about music? Try this totally free site. Here you can take an online class on music and when you are finished, you will have a basic understanding of how it works.

Fractal Music: The Sound of Chaos

http://www.discovery.com/stories/technology/fractals/fractals.html

Those who hear fractal music for the first time find it hard to describe, using terms like otherworldly, bizarre, or fantastic. Come to this site to see what chaos can sound like. Here these erie sounds that somehow make sense.

Hop Pop Town

http://www.kids-space.org/HPT/

A visit to this site is a must, especially if you like to see new things the Internet can do. Children are encouraged to create and expand their innate musical ability. While aimed at children ages 3 to 10, those older might find this enjoyable, too.

Kidsongs Online

http://www.kidsongs.com/

Use the Song Search to find out which products contain your favorite Kidsongs music, video, or song. You can even download a coloring sheet, send a message to your favorite characters, and more!

Lycos Zone Kool Karaoke for Kids

http://eatsleepmusic.lycos.com/

Singers, this site was designed just for you. The posted words allow you to sing along to the music. You can choose a song from a long list of old favorites— "Alphabet Soup," "The Ants Go Marching," "The Old Woman Who Swallowed A Fly," and more.

Make It At Home - Musical Instruments

http://www.childrensmuseum.org/artsworkshop/offline.html

Click on Musical Instruments to see how to create these instruments with easy-to-find and inexpensive materials to form a family orchestra. The instruments include a PVC flute, flimsy box fiddle, deep base fiddle, rainbow piano, and the drum set.

Morton Subotnick's Creating Music

http://www.creatingmusic.com/

Maybe you would like to be a musician but you don't know how to begin. Try this site to get you going in the right direction. The Rhythm Band allows you to write music, edit, choose instruments, and decide on the tempo. And when they say "play" with music, you really can do that. Try it!

Mudcat Café - Kids

http://www.mudcat.org/kids/

Children will love this music site where they can try out instruments. Become a drummer. Try a banjo or a fiddle. Be sure you try the many, many Digitrad Kids Songs. You'll be singing for sure!

Musical Instruments of the World

http://www.eyeneer.com/World/Instruments/index.html

The International Music Archives presents musical instruments of the world through photographs, sound samples, and text. Some of the countries include: Africa, North Africa, West Asia, East Asia, South Asia, Southeast Asia, and Europe. Some of the instruments you will be introduced to are the arched harp, double pit xylophone, harp-lute, lute, and wooden slit-drum.

Music Notes: An Interactive Online Musical Experience

http://library.thinkquest.org/15413/

This comprehensive site includes learning experiences from reading music to exploring styles of music from Rock to Bach to learning about instruments.

On Air Concert

http://www.kids-space.org/air/air.html

This is a great site for those interested in music by and for children. In fact, children under 16 years of age can submit music to this site. (Your computer must be capable of recording to do this.) If you can't hear, don't despair. This site will direct you to files and browsers needed to run their music by simply following their easy-to-use directions.

Piano Education Page - Just for Kids

http://www.unm.edu/~loritaf/pnokids.html

Are you taking piano lessons? This website is just for you. You can find helpful tips to make your piano lessons go more smoothly. Read the Tip of the Month to get an edge on your skills. If you have a question for a piano teacher, you can submit it to the site's piano teacher and get a response. Try the many links for other cool piano sites.

Piano on the Net

http://www.artdsm.com/piano/index.html

Have you been thinking about taking piano lessons? If so, try this site and you will feel like you have a personal tutor to help you learn how to play the piano. You will find 34 lessons divided into beginner, intermediate, and advanced lessons.

PlayMusic.org

http://www.playmusic.org/

Are you interested in the orchestra? Do you know the parts of an orchestra? Do you have a favorite instrument? Come to this site and see the entire orchestra. Click on one of the sections of the orchestra—woodwinds, brass, percussion, or strings—and learn about the individual instruments. Additionally, learn about composers and musicians.

Radio Disney

http://disney.go.com/radiodisney/index_main.html

Here kids can request a song, enter Radio Disney sweepstakes, get the scoop on the hottest artists, read bios of their favorite bands, vote for their favorite songs, and even listen to Radio Disney on their computer. Pretty cool, huh?

Scratch Simulator

http://www.turntables.de/start.htm

Think you're a good DJ? Try out your skills with this cool virtual DJ booth. Includes turntables, scratching samples, sound clips, lighting effects, and much more. A one-of-a-kind site!

Spinner.com

http://www.spinner.com/

This popular Internet radio site allows you to listen to music on your computer while you are working or playing online. Simply sign up and download the player, then you'll have access to over 150 music channels and more than 375,000 songs. Best of all, it's free!

Sprocket Works

http://www.sprocketworks.com/

Click on the Music link found on the right sidebar menu. You can learn about reading and writing music, sharps and flats, train your eyes and ears, and learn Bach. Go for it at this great site!

The Wiggles

http://www.thewiggles.com.au/

What is Red, Yellow, Blue, and Purple and a lot of fun? It's The Wiggles! Find out when The Wiggles will be performing near your home, get some background info on each Wiggle, and more.

Yahoo! Music

http://music.yahoo.com/

Check out this site for daily news, reviews, charts and more. Link to downloadable MP3s, listen to online concerts and interviews, or find out who's on tour in your area. This site has everything you need to know to stay up on the music scene.

Ocean & Sea Life

All About Sharks

http://www.EnchantedLearning.com/subjects/sharks/

This comprehensive site about sharks is a great starting point for everything you want to know about this creature of the deep. At this site you will find the following information and more: size, anatomy, variety of sharks (and there is a long list), teeth, anatomy, diet, and shark attacks.

All About Whales

http://www.EnchantedLearning.com/subjects/whales/

If you like or want to learn about whales, come to this site. You will find information sheets about whales, simple whale printout sheets, whale myths, and more.

Aquarius

http://www.uncwil.edu/nurc/

Aquarius is the world's only underwater laboratory operational in our world's oceans, and is located adjacent to a coral reef in the Florida Keys National Marine Sanctuary. This site is explains their many missions. If you click on "Information" you will be able to take an online tour.

Great Sharks for Kids

http://www.greatsharks.com/

The creator of this website on sharks starts out with general information that is appropriate for a 5th grade student. As the reader moves along and gets into more in-depth information, the reading level and the amount of information increases. This is a solid site for learning about sharks.

Icebergs - Antarctic Adventure

http://www.antarctic.com.au/

Would you like to take a journey to Antarctica? Come to this website for your virtual trip. Click the Encyclopaedia Antarctica link, then choose the Physical Environment link, then the Southern Ocean to learn about icebergs and how they are formed.

International Year of the Ocean - Kid's and Teacher's Resources

http://www.yoto98.noaa.gov/kids.htm

This fantastic site is loaded with great stuff for kids. There are activities "books" related to different topics, like Puffy the Puffer's Fun Facts, The Whale (Kohola), and The Plover (Kolea). You will also find information on endangered sea lions and seals, fish, marine debris, El Niño, and more.

Observing a Coral Reef

http://www.eduweb.com/jason/briefing.html

This Digital Lab focuses on coral reefs in Bermuda. Using images from Dr. Robbie Smith's field research, you will record and analyze reef data from 1993 and 1997. You can use this data to assess the health of the reef. Read the project briefing, or go directly to Dr. Smith's field site to select the coral images to study.

Oceanic Research

http://www.oceanicresearch.org/

Visit this site to learn more about the oceans of the world and the life therein. Click on the Education link and you will find great information on ocean life— sponges, mollusks, sharks, and more.

Oceanography

http://www.onr.navy.mil/focus/ocean/default.html

Everything that you want to know about oceans must be at this site, which presents the information in an organized manner. Topics include the ocean floor, waves, ocean life, habitats, ocean water, and current research.

Planet Ocean

http://school.discovery.com/schooladventures/planetocean/index.html

Thousands of incredible and bizarre creatures have made the ocean their home. Discover what it takes for these amazing animals to survive this underwater world. Learn about the blue whale, the barracuda, and the tubeworm. Vote for who you think should be a marine megastar!

Rodale's Scuba Diving

http://www.scubadiving.com/

Everything you want to know about scuba diving—equipment, training and safety, photography, locations for dives—can be found at this site. Be sure to check out the tip of the day, special features, or links to other sites.

SeaWeb

http://www.seaweb.org/

Do you want to know what is happening with the oceans of the world? Visit this site for the latest news. The latest on oil spills and other challenges are reported here. Listen to Peter Benchly give the latest sea report on the radio, too.

Tide Pool Page

http://web.mit.edu/corrina/tpool/

Tide pools are fascinating environments. If you can't visit one, take a virtual tour via this site. If you can visit one, learn what you can do to make your visit less of an impact on this precious environment.

Treasures@Sea

http://www.fi.edu/fellows/fellow8/dec98/main.html

Most oceanographers do their work on boats in the ocean. We won't be able to do our research from a boat, but we can dive into these Treasure Hunts to learn facts about the ocean. So strap on your scuba gear, get your goggles ready, and jump right in to see what treasures await you at sea!

U.S. Coast Guard Kids' Corner

http://www.uscg.mil/hq/g-cp/kids/kidindx.html

This site contains many links that relate to the Coast Guard, boating, and more. Be sure to take a look at the photo albums.

Venturing into Hawaii's Coral Reef

http://library.thinkquest.org/J002237/

Mahalo! "Venture into Hawaii's Coral Reefs" validates the fact that Hawaii's coral reef is indeed the tropical rainforest of the sea. As you journey through this website, you will learn about coral reefs, coral fish, and other creatures.

Pictures & Photography

Kodak

http://www.kodak.com/

If you are interested in photography this site is a must-see. View the picture of the day, download a screensaver, pick up helpful tips for taking pictures, and browse the archive of awesome photographs for any occasion. You can create your own photogreetings and even store your personal pictures at the site.

Oatmeal Box Pinhole Photography

http://www.nh.ultranet.com/~stewoody/

Do you have an empty Quaker Oats box and aluminum can? You can make a camera with those two items and a roll of film. You can make a darkroom out of a bathroom and you are set to be a photographer. Check this site out for more details.

Shutterfly

http://www.shutterfly.com/index.jsp

Transfer your digital pictures onto this site, then get creative with them! You can add a unique border or message, crop the photos, remove red eye, and more. Plus, turn your pictures into printed greeting cards or order high-quality prints.

SnapFish

http://www.snapfish.com/

Upload your digital photos, then create an online album to share with friends and family. This complete photo service offers film developing, printing, storing, and sharing online, all for free in the United States. You pay only for shipping and handling of your prints.

Preschool

Arthur

http://www.pbs.org/wgbh/arthur/

Fans of the brainy aardvark can't miss this site, which gives kids an insight into the lives of Arthur and his friends, and will even test their knowledge of Arthur trivia in the Brain's Brain Game. Kids can send electronic postcards, learn to draw Arthur, play Buster's ice cream game of fun and sprinkles, and more. Don't miss Francine's PlayMaker, which gives kids expert tips on how to put on a play at home (it even includes Arthur scripts!).

Arts and Crafts Projects

http://www.familyplay.com

There are all kinds of art activities at this site. Choose Art Projects from the menu and click go. Try the Clothespin Dragonfly, Crayon Rubbing Placemat, Door Knob Sign, Name Medallion, and more. Children will love the simplicity of the art activities presented here.

Babybug Magazine

http://www.cricketmag.com

Babybug Magazine, written for the 6-month to two-year-old, is a delightful site. When entering the site, click on the first sign and at the next screen click on Babybug. Upon entering the site you will want to check out the Parents area first for information. Try the Play and Sing site and, of course, do the Read Together with your favorite child.

Barney Online

http://www.barney.com/

If your child's a fan of the infamous purple dinosaur, she'll find plenty to do inside Barney's online house. Little ones can play hide-and-seek as they navigate to different areas of Barney's site, where they'll find Barney stories, music (he sings "I Love You" in nine languages!), and more. We liked reading the answers to Barney's fan mail!

Clifford

http://www.pbs.org/clifford/

When they visit Clifford in his online doghouse, kids can read-along with Emily Elizabeth in an interactive storybook, print out pages to color, and play educational games. We like the Behind the Scenes area where kids can learn to draw Clifford themselves and meet the cast of the TV show. Did you know that Clifford's voice is John Ritter of *Three's Company* fame?

Dragon Tales

http://www.pbs.org/dragontales/

If you wish with all your heart to fly with dragons in a land apart, this is the site for you! Choose a dragon to fly with and let the dragon games begin. This immersive online version of Dragon Land is full of games, songs, and other creative learning activities.

Idea Box - Early Childhood Education and Activity Resources

http://www.theideabox.com/

This site is a great resource for anyone interested in early childhood education. Try the Great Idea for Today—it may be some craft activity, game or food fun. You may want to participate in the monthly contest. Take a peek at the Site of the Week. They are archived so you can review previously highlighted sites.

Kids Next Door

http://www.hud.gov/kids/

This preschool or kindergarten site teaches children about the roles of community members through the "What's My Job" activity. There are virtual tours to community facilities—e.g., the library or the park. Children even have an opportunity to learn about the homeless—who and where they are and what kids can do to help. HUD sponsors this site.

KinderCrafts for Toddlers, Preschoolers, and Kindergartners

http://www.enchantedlearning.com/crafts/toddler/

The crafts projects presented at this site are for toddler, preschoolers, and kindergartners. With adult supervision and guidance, even toddlers can make most of these simple projects. The crafts use materials found around the house, like egg cartons, cardboard, paper, boxes, string, crayons, paint, glue, etc.

Kindle Park

http://www.kindlepark.com/

Kindle Park is a perfect site for the preschooler and his or her parents. As you enter the site, you are greeted with happy music and colorful graphics. There are activities, books, videos, and more to inspire young and old alike as you navigate through the wonderful activities. You will want to bookmark this one!

Ladybug Magazine

http://www.cricketmag.com/cgi-bin/cricket.cgi?tpl=index

Ladybug Magazine, written for the 2-6 year old, is a delightful site. When entering the site, click on the first sign and at the next screen click on Ladybug. When you get to the Ladybug site, go to the Play and Sing site and have some fun. Don't forget to check out the "Read Together."

Lycos Zone Kool Karaoke for Kids

http://eatsleepmusic.lycos.com

Sing it loud! Come on in and sing along to your favorite songs! Choose your song—the site includes Alphabet Soup, The Ants Go Marching, The Old Woman Who Swallowed A Fly, and many more familiar songs.

NickJr.com

http://www.nickjr.com/kids/flash_site/index.jhtml

This site integrates kids' favorite Nick Jr. characters into games, stories, music, and art activities. Little Bear, Blue, Franklin, Dora, Maisy, Kipper, Maggie, Little Bill, and Bob the Builder all find their homes here. While you're playing online, tune into NickJr.com radio for some preschool pop!

Noddy

http://www.pbs.org/kids/noddy/

Visit Noddy's site for plenty of activities designed for 3- to 7-year-olds. Older kids can play on their own, while younger kids will have more fun with a caregiver playing alongside them. Like the show, the site has a special focus on music education.

PenPal Box

http://www.ks-connection.org/penpal/penpal.html

Would you like to have a penpal? This is the perfect site to get you started. You can choose a penpal right out of a PenPal Box according to your age. Preschooler and kindergarten would use PenPal Box 1. If you have any questions be sure to check the Guide Bear's PenPal Box Help.

Playhouse Disney

http://disney.go.com/park/bases/playhousebase/today/flash/index.html

This sunny virtual playground is designed for the preschool set. Here, little ones can interact with their favorite characters from Bear in the Big Blue House, Out of the Box, The Book of Pooh, Rolie Polie Olie, and PB & J Otter. A parent's guide gives ideas on how to extend the activities offline.

Pre-Reading Skills

http://www.familyplay.com/activities/actPrereading.html

Help a child to become better reader by giving him/her some basic skills. This can be done through providing students with simple activities like letter recognition, vowel sounds, consonant blends, and more. These simple activities can give children an edge as they start reading.

Preschool Math

http://www.familyplay.com/activities/actPremath.html

If you would like some fun activities to use with a preschool child, then try this site. You will find activities that use basic household items. Subjects include: categorizing, measuring, matching, and patterning.

Mama Lisa's House of Nursery Rhymes

http://mamalisa.com/house/

You can read the familiar nursery rhymes at this site—Peter, Peter, Pumpkin Eater; Hey Diddle Diddle; Pop Goes the Weasel; and more. Some of the rhymes have a surprise sound.

SesameStreet.com

http://www.sesameworkshop.org/sesamestreet/

From tickling Elmo to making breakfast with Cookie Monster, there's no shortage of fun on SesameStreet.com. This site is filled with games, stories, coloring pages, and other activities for you and your child to enjoy together. This kind of fun can also lead to learning—kids practice letters, numbers, shapes, sorting, and more.

Small Motor Skills

http://www.familyplay.com/activities/actSmallmotor.html

Young children need to practice their small motor skills and the more help we can give them, the better! This site has many activities that concentrate on the small motor skills like eye-hand coordination, hand and finger movement, balance, and more.

Fun With Spot

http://www.funwithspot.com/house.asp?locale=US

Home to the playful yellow dog, this site is ideal for young children. Simple drawings (just like in the books) make navigation easy. There's plenty of fun to be had at a party, the beach, the farm, or the park.

Seussville Games

http://www.randomhouse.com/seussville/games/

Here are lots of games for you to play
To keep you entertained all day!
The greatest games you've ever seen
To play on your computer screen.
Plus some games you print out and then
You play them with paper and pen.

Tree Homes

http://www.lhs.berkeley.edu/kids/

This is a perfect site for non-readers because they only need to click to find the creatures who live in, on, or near trees. From the Kids page choose Tree Homes— upper right corner—to get started.

Reading & Language Arts
General

Barbie StoryMaker

http://www.barbie.com/Activities/Storymaker/

Hey, Barbie lovers! Here is an opportunity to write a story with the StoryMaker's help. Begin by selecting a character, a mood for the character and a setting. The story begins and you can sit back and watch. This site is great for a young, budding storyteller.

Beanstalk

http://www.kids-space.org/bean/bean.html

Beanstalk is a place to show your imagination and creativity through a picture or a story that is dedicated to the original child author. Even when two children have never met, they will be able create a very original picture book through Beanstalk. In fact, most of Beanstalk works are done by who live in different countries. Check the Help page for further instructions.

Between the Lions

http://www.pbs.org/wgbh/lions/

Each week this site features an "adventure," which includes one story and a dozen related games that target reading, writing, listening, and speaking. The original games and stories are based on the TV series and all follow the week's theme and curriculum goals. The site is updated every Monday with a new Web adventure.

The Randolph Caldecott Medal

http://www.ala.org/alsc/caldecott.html

Visit this site to see the latest book awarded the Randolph Caldecott Medal. At the bottom of the screen you will find links to past winners and a quick, printable list of all Caldecott Medal winners from 1938-2000. Read about the criteria used for determining the artist of the most distinguished American picture book for children.

Children's Book Garden

http://childrensbookgarden.com/

Thinking about getting a new book to read? Check out the reviews at this site. You can look at them by age level, author, or title. The author of the site is a former classroom teacher.

Cool Word of the Day

http://features.learningkingdom.com/word/

Not only can you build your vocabulary with a daily visit to this site, but you can also learn about the origins of words and phrases. This site is appropriate for 7+ grade levels. If you want to make sure you see the Cool Word of the Day, sign up for the free subscription.

FakeOut

http://www.eduplace.com/fakeout/

Do you want to increase your vocabulary? Would you like to test out the vocabulary you already have? Try this site. There are two ways to play it. First, you can guess the definition of the listed words. Or, you can write definitions for words. Whichever game you choose to play, you can choose the grade level most suitable for you. Past games are available, too.

Fairy Godmother

http://www.fairygodmother.com/

This is a most unusual site but it will capture your imagination and spur it on to wonderful creativity. You will land in the Night Garden where you can wish on a star, read a poem about fairies, or you can have a visit with Mrs. Teacups. But don't neglect the Day Garden where you will find activities which will help you unleash your artistic nature—be it in words, virtual painting or make believe.

First Grade Author Study

http://www.ash.udel.edu/incoming/west1/authors/kidpage2.html

Pretend your class will decide who the author should be at this your school's Author Program. Although you are encouraged to work in small groups, you can work alone on this project as you research who is the best author for the event. Authors, their books, appropriate links (scroll down to find the links), and presentation ideas are suggested.

For Young Writers

http://www.inkspot.com/young/

Are you interested in doing some serious writing? Then this is the source for you! Take part in a monthly poll, read the Feature Article where you will find helpful writing tips, visit the young writers chat room, or submit an idea to the Hopper.

The Global Campfire

http://www.indiana.edu/~eric_rec/fl/pcto/campfire.html

The tradition of this campfire site is simple: [1] read one of the stories that interests you, [2] add the next part of the story, and [3] check back later to see if your contribution has been added to the story. It is a fun way to write and also contribute to a larger project.

Global Story Train

http://www.kids-space.org/

The Global Story Train demonstrates an excellent use for the Internet. Students from around the world can write stories together. One student begins the story and another student adds to it and passes it on to another. Read the stories by clicking on the train at this home page.

Golden Books Fun Factory

http://www.goldenbooks.com/

This site contains a Story Wheel, Games and Activities, Coloring Fun, e-Magic Pages, and Jokes and Riddles. At the Print Factory, parents must register and are charged ninety-nine cents a month for unlimited printing of activity pages. If you would like a screen saver for your Windows or Macintosh computer go to e-Stuff.

Grammar Gorillas

http://www.funbrain.com/grammar/

Grammar, some think, can be boring. Not here! Play grammar games at this site. If you are just learning about nouns and verbs, stick with the beginner's level. If you are ready for more, hit the advanced link. You will have fun and learn about grammar, too.

Grammar Rock

http://www.apocalypse.org/pub/u/gilly/Schoolhouse_Rock/HTML/grammar/grammar.html

You remember these songs, now share them with your kids. This site has all the Schoolhouse Rock grammar songs: Unpack Your Adjectives (How Adjectives Modify Nouns), Conjunction Junction (How Conjunctions Hook Up Words and Phrases and Clauses), Interjections (Handy Interjections Like "Yow!", "Ouch!", and "Hey!"), Verb: That's What's Happening (A Verb Tells It Like It Is, To Be, To See, To Feel, To Live), and more.

Graphic Organizers

http://www.eduplace.com/kids/hme/graphorg/

When you write a paper, are your thoughts going in many different directions? Try using a graphic organizer to help you form in an organized manner. This site contains more than 20 organizers to help improve your writing skills.

I Spy

http://www.scholastic.com/ispy/

If you're a fan of Jean Marzollo and Walter Wick, extend the fun with I Spy online. These riddles will give you plenty more to look for in the books you already have at home. Plus, use the interactive game to build an *I Spy* picture, then print your creation or mail it to a friend. Or, write a riddle to go along with the *I Spy* picture of the month.

Junior Scholastic Kids

http://www.scholastic.com/kids

This site is full of great fun for literary-minded kids. Play I Spy online or Make Your Own Comic with Captain Underpants. Don't miss the News Zones, The Baby Sitter's Club, Clifford the Big Red Dog, and the many other fun options present on the site.

Kids@Random

http://www.randomhouse.com/kids/

Find games, screensavers, news, and more at this site dedicated to Random House's children's book properties. Play the *Green Eggs & Ham* scramble game, join Arthur on the highway, or visit Jack and Annie in the Magic Tree House. Plus, link to mini-sites for the Berenstain Bears, Arthur, Junie B. Jones, Dragon Tales, Star Wars, Sweet Valley, and Thomas & Friends.

Kidnews

http://www.kidnews.com/

Kidnews.com is a free news and writing service for students and teachers from around the globe and has published thousands of young authors from every continent (except Antarctica)! Anyone may submit whether a review, journalism piece, short story, poem, sports critique, real life accounts, opinions, or advice to fellow kids. Every submission, just like at a publishing house, is edited and reviewed for content and language before being posted.

Language Links

http://polyglot.lss.wisc.edu/lss

For the serious language learner, this site is one you need to visit—just click on Language Links. Here you will find specific links for various languages—Multi-Language Sites, African Languages and Literature, Asian Studies, Classics, English as a Second/Foreign Language, French, Germanic Languages, Hebrew and Semitic Studies, Italian, Portuguese, Quechua, Scandinavian Studies, Slavic, and Spanish.

Lit Cafe

http://library.thinkquest.org/17500/

English teachers, librarians, and students: This one's for you! A well-executed, excellent site that provides basic biographies of some of the most influential writers of the western world, a guide to literary terms and devices (with examples), grammar, roots of words back to the Latin and Greek, English fundamentals (including spelling), and literary devices.

Little Planet Times

http://littleplanettimes.com

The Little Planet Times is a newspaper for kids and by kids, with a little help from the characters on the Little Planet. Each issue has a central theme for children to read about, to write about, to discuss, and to learn. The ideas, the stories, and the creations that young writers submit are published and folded into every new issue. To begin, we suggest that you first read the front page story, then click on the Activities Button at the bottom of the first page.

Lycos Zone Rhymezone

http://www.rhymezone.com/

This is a simple site, but oh so helpful. Type in the word you want to rhyme. Make sure Find Rhyme is showing in the pull-down menu and click Go get it. If there is a rhyming word to match your word, it will appear. Note that you can also get other words—synonyms, definitions, phrases, and more.

Scrabble

http://www.hasbroscrabble.com

If you like Scrabble, check out this website. Here you will find an online Scrabble Dictionary, the official rules of the game, word lists, and Skill Builders to improve your thinking. The Anagram Builder will improve your word building skills. When you are finished with this site you'll play like a pro!

The John Newbery Medal

http://www.ala.org/alsc/newbery.html

Visit this site to see the latest book awarded the John Newbery Medal. Links at the bottom of the screen will take you to past winners and a quick, printable list of all Newbery Medal Winners from 1922-2000. Discover the criteria used for determining the author who has written the best American literature for children.

Paradigm Online Writing Assistant

http://www.powa.org/

Paradigm is intended to be useful for all writers, from inexperienced to advanced. To get the most from the website, take time to explore its components. Choose a topic that interests you, read the discussion, do an activity, move to another topic. Sense how the topics relate to your own needs and interests. Some writers, for instance, will want to practice editing, while others will be more interested in discovering ideas.

Portfolio, Accordion Fold and Box Books

http://www.mcgehee.k12.la.us/AnthWeb/Port.html

Would you like to make your stories look like real books? This site will show you how to do that. The diagrams will help you to create great looking books. You might want to give them as gifts to family members and friends.

Pre-Reading Skills

http://www.familyplay.com/activities/actPrereading.html

Help your child to become a better reader by giving him or her some basic skills. This can be done through providing simple activities like letter recognition, vowel sounds, consonant blends, and more.

Reading Dimension

http://www.eduplace.com/kids/book/index.html

At this site children are encouraged to read a book and participate in follow-up activities. Questions are posed to the reader to extend the thinking that goes into the reading experience. There is a link to information on the author and, best of all, there is a discussion area that can only be entered once the book has been read.

Shelf III - Folk Tales

http://www.kids-space.org/folk/folk.html

If you like to read folk tales, read some from North America or around the world on this site. Do you know a folk tale that you have heard from your family or relatives? Have you read folk tales about your town, city, or country? If you know one, send it to this folk tale site for publishing on their website.

Story Book

http://www.kids-space.org/story/story.html

Story Book takes kids' stories and publishes them on this website. Just like in a library, students can choose a shelf and read stories. The shelves include stories based on monthly material and original stories, poems, journals, play scripts, and folktales. Stories from previous years are archived and can be read too.

SIGNhear Website

http://library.thinkquest.org/10202/

This website was designed to promote the use of Sign language as a form of communication, just like a foreign language. At this site you can learn basic American Sign Language. In addition to the ASL fingerspelling alphabet, you will find the 200 most used signs.

Student Packet Mystery

http://tqjunior.thinkquest.org/5109/

This website is about mysteries. There are two story starters you can finish and two mysteries you can solve. There is also information about what a mystery is, and a few vocabulary words you can learn. The creators of the website included some of their favorite mystery books.

Vintage Reading Group Center

http://www.randomhouse.com/vintage/read/

Sometimes when we read a great book we just want to talk about it to someone who has also read the book. Other times we may read a book and have some questions about it. That's what this site is for. There are lots of opportunities for interaction, book recommendations and overviews, and more. We recommend this site for mature readers.

Wacky Web Tales

http://www.eduplace.com/tales/index.html

If you are a budding student author, this is a great place to submit your stories. Also, if you want to know what your peers are writing, check in once in awhile and read the current postings. Read the Writing Tips that offer guidelines and help.

Webtime Stories

http://www.kn.pacbell.com/wired/webtime/

Webtime Stories is an annotated collection of websites for people who love children's literature. Though there is nothing quite like reading a good book, the Internet combines the printed word with graphics, sounds, interactivity and animation to create rich and memorable reading experiences.

Weekly Reader Galaxy

http://www.weeklyreader.com/features/kid.html

At this site you can read the latest news, take a weekly poll (and read the results from last week's), and answer the day's Geoquiz. You can also click on your grade level and find information that relates to the latest issue of Weekly Reader.

Write on Readers

http://library.thinkquest.org/J001156/

Write on Readers invites you to visit their site to gain a love of reading and writing, and an appreciation for authors and illustrators. You will have the help of hosts Buster Book and Penny Pencil as you tour through this amazing site. Who knows? You may become a writer after you finish viewing this site.

Writing Den - Tips-O-Matic

http://www2.actden.com/writ_den/

If you need to work on writing skills, visit this site for some excellent suggestions. Junior high students click on tips-o-matic to find headings. This site offers explanations and excellent examples for clarification.

Reading & Language Arts
Authors

Judy Blume

http://www.judyblume.com/links.html

Are you a Judy Blume fan? Come to her website and find the latest information on her books. Be sure to click on the Kids Page because you will find some interesting facts about the people behind her books. Find out who The *Pain* and the *Great One* are!

Jan Brett

http://www.janbrett.com/

Jan Brett has a delightful site for the readers of her books. Try the activities—you will find projects, coloring pages, flash cards, calendars, audio files, a Hedgie screensaver, and more. Subscribe to Hedgie's Home Page for updates on the website. This is only the beginning.

Betsy Byars

http://www.betsybyars.com/

Visit Betsy Byars' site and find some of the background information on her and the many books she has authored. If you are an aspiring author, make sure to read her writing tips.

Official Eric Carle Website

http://www.eric-carle.com/

Did you ever read *Brown Bear, Brown Bear, What Do You See?*, or *The Very Hungry Caterpillar?* Visit the Eric Carle site and you will be able to read the many questions that have been asked of him. You can also check out the *Caterpillar Express: An Occasional Newsletter from Eric Carle.*

Vicki Cobb Kids Science Page

http://www.vickicobb.com/

Want to have some fun? Visit the Vicki Cobb Kids Science Page and do some experimenting. The author has presented a science activity (e.g., the coin flip trick you can't lose) from each of her science books. You can write her a message, too!

Jean Craighead George

http://www.jeancraigheadgeorge.com/

Remember *Julie of the Wolves* or *My Side of the Mountain*? Read about this author and her love of nature that is clearly shown in her books. Make sure you see the audio, video, and photo links, as well as the writing tips.

Roald Dahl

http://www.roalddahl.com/index2.htm

At this amazing official Roald Dahl site, your friends Mathilda, James, and the BFG have prepared mystic and marvelous surprises that will entrance, delight, intrigue, astonish, and perplex. Don't miss out on this one!

Mercer Mayer's Little Critter

http://www.littlecritter.com/

On this official site, kids can learn about the author, Mercer Mayer, and check out the art gallery, favorite jokes, coloring book, and movies.

Robert Munsch Website

http://www.robertmunsch.com/

Check out the books Mr. Munsch has written, read his biography and poems. One of the special features of this site is the virtual story room. Drop by and hear stories written by Robert Munsch.

Sheldon Oberman Writing and Storytelling

http://www.mbnet.mb.ca/~soberman/

Would you like to challenge and train yourself as a poet and songwriter? Visit this website and look for the Kids link. After each activity you will find the answer key and the author's thoughts.

Dav Pilkey's Website O' Fun

http://www.pilkey.com/

Warning! Dav warns that this site is silly—probably too silly! (Adults, house-plants, and small animals must be accompanied by a child if they want to visit.) This site is full of great fun. It shouldn't be missed.

Random House: E.L. Konigsburg

http://www.randomhouse.com/teachers/authors/koni.html

Read a brief bio, see her photo, get a list of her books, and learn fun facts about this notable author.

Jon Scieszka and Lane Smith

http://www.chucklebait.com/

Learn all about the lives of Jon and Lane, read excerpts from their books, sign up for their mailing list, send them a message, ask Beefsnakstik your burning questions, and play the super-fun rock, paper, scissors games. A site that's just as fun as the books!

J.R.R. Tolkien

http://www.houghtonmifflinbooks.com/

The J.R.R. Tolkien featured website (click on the link on the home page) created by Houghton Mifflin Books gives some background information on Tolkien and his book. After you look around, try the links to find other richly developed sites on this author.

Mark Twain

http://www.cmgww.com/

To find the Mark Twain site, scroll through the top menu for Mark Twain. At the Mark Twain site you will find biographical information, some of his witty quotations, photos, a list of his writings, links to other Mark Twain sites, and more.

Audrey Wood Clubhouse

http://www.audreywood.com

Come to this delightful website and meet the author of many great books—*Silly Sally*, *Bright and Early Thursday Evening*, and *Heckedy Peg*. There are activities, opportunities to meet the artists and author, sections for parents and teachers, and more.

Reading & Language Arts
Online Books, Poetry & Stories

Atlantic Unbound: Poetry Pages

http://www.theatlantic.com/unbound

Poetry lovers, this is a must-see site. Many people are familiar with Atlantic Monthly but they don't know about this wonderful Atlantic Monthly Internet poetry page. To get there, click on Poetry Pages in the sidebar. Old, familiar poems are featured along with the new.

Aesop's Fables

http://www.umass.edu/aesop/

From the familiar "Wolf in Sheep's Clothing" to the less familiar "The Two Crabs," this site presents almost 40 of the fables. In addition to the traditional version, a modern version is presented. The graphics enhance the visit to this site.

Around the World in 80 Days: A Geography Adventure

http://library.thinkquest.org/J002459F/

How would you like to travel around the whole world in just 80 days? That is what Phileas Fogg did in the famous book by Jules Verne, *Around the World in 80 Days*. This website provides information on Fogg and the countries he visited on his 80-day travels. Bon Voyage!

Book Adventure

http://www.bookadventure.com/

Book Adventure is a free reading incentive program dedicated to encouraging kids in grades K-8 to read. With the help of Rex Reader and Bailey Bookmark, kids have more than 4,000 of the most popular and acclaimed titles from which to choose.

Contemporary Writing for Children and Young Adults

http://www.acs.ucalgary.ca/~dkbrown/storcont.html

This site contains many stories by well-known authors, as well as some who are new to children's literature. Some examples of the stories available include: *The Goodie Bag, How the Grinch Stole Christmas,* and *Theodore Tugboat.*

The Funny Forty

http://www.nesbitt.com/poetry/

If you like to laugh, visit this poetry site. Some of the poems included at this site are: Things You Don't Need to Know, At Standing Still I Have a Skill, Benson Baxter Brought His Bowling Ball, and Zzzzz. Kenn Nesbitt writes great poetry and he continually adds to this site; a return visit is a must.

Heidi by Johanna Spyri

http://www.geocities.com/EnchantedForest/Glade/8905/

Heidi fans, this site is for you. Links that relate to *Heidi* include: Switzerland information and map, the loft, the goats, recipes that make you think of Switzerland, the wildflowers that grow in the mountain fields, and much more.

Kids Love a Mystery

http://www.KidsLoveAMystery.com/

Do you love a good mystery? Come to this site and read online mysteries and try to solve them. Check out the link to the Nancy Drew Mysteries too. It's a fun site.

Laura Ingalls Wilder, Frontier Girl

http://webpages.marshall.edu/~irby1/laura.htmlx

Through the stories written by Laura Ingalls Wilder, readers can learn about pioneer families who worked hard just to survive throughout the midwest states (mainly Wisconsin, Minnesota, Kansas, and South Dakota). This site includes background information on the author.

Legends and Myths

http://www.gov.nt.ca/kids/legend/legends.htm

Storytelling is an important way of passing on history and culture in the Northwest Territories. At this site you can read tales from the north, Inuit legends, the book of Dene, and more.

Local Legend and Folktales

http://www.ash.udel.edu/ash

This site highlights some of the local legends and folktales of New Jersey. If you want to find legends and folktales in your area, you will find some good suggestions by clicking the "More Stuff To Investigate" link. Use the Exhibit Hall and the Peoples and Culture links to take you to the site.

The Many Faces of Alice

http://www.dalton.org/ms/alice/

Several fourth grade classes have done extensive studies of *Alice's Adventures in Wonderland* by Lewis Carroll. See the results of their study at this site. If you are an Alice in Wonderland enthusiast, this site is for you.

Poetry Lane

http://www.poetrylane.com/

There are lots of poems found on this site. Children will love the topics and the graphics that accompany the poems. When you run out of poems (that should take awhile), try the archive or the links for other poetry.

Project Gutenberg

http://promo.net/pg/

Get books, mainly classics, online at the Project Gutenberg website. You can browse by author or title. Be aware the only books that can be digitized and put online are those that no longer have copyright protection.

Rat Tales

http://library.thinkquest.org/J002079F/

Rat Tales is based on the Newbery-award winning book, *Mrs. Frisby and the Rats of NIMH* by Robert C. O'Brien. The book touches on the subjects of intelligence, both animal and human, the ethics of animal experimentation, problem solving, and simple machines. While reading the book, students can visit the website to test their reading comprehension with interactive questions, solve math problems based on situations from the book, and much more.

Reading Zone Internet Public Library

http://www.ipl.org/youth/

Calling all readers! Come to the Reading Zone to find links to picture books, authors, books, and for the youngest reader, Story Hour.

Rebecca of Sunnybrook Farm

http://www.knowledgerush.com/books

Find the title in the Children's section on the entry page. This Kate Douglas Wiggins story is about Rebecca who was raised on a farm, but was forced to go live with her rather unloving aunt. With her happy, endearing ways, it is not long before Rebecca wins over her aunt and the entire town. This is a delightful story that is perfect for readers of any age.

A Tale of Tulips

http://www.capcan.ca/english/youth

A Tale of Tulips is a fairly tale about a country that was invaded. Since the royal family was in danger it was decided that they needed to flee to a distant land. And so the story goes. While kids read the story they can click on highlighted words and get real facts that inspired the fairy tale. There are two games that go with the story.

Treasure Island

http://www.ofcn.org/cyber.serv/resource/bookshelf/treas10/

The complete text of the famed book by Robert Louis Stevenson is on this site, divided into chapters.

The Velveteen Rabbit or How Toys Become Real

http://www.writepage.com/velvet.htm

Read the delightful Margery Williams' tale online. This is the beloved story of the toy bunny who wanted to be real and loved by his young boy owner. When the boy became ill, the rabbit was thrown away in the trash. Read the sweet story to find out what happens.

Reading & Language Arts
Harry Potter

CBC4Kids Harry Potter Page!

http://www.cbc4kids.ca

Would you like to meet the author J.K.Rowling? Well, then this is the site for you.
Listen to the interview of J.K.Rowling conducted by kids at a live webcast.
Included on the site are several other interviews and links to information related to
the author and her books.

Harry Potter and the Sorcerer's Stone

http://harrypotter.warnerbros.com

Find information on the movie that is being made out of the first of JK Rowling's
magical Harry Potter books. Read news releases, find out about the actors selected
to play Harry and his fellow characters, and sign up for information on the movie.
(The latter requires an e-mail address.)

Harry Potter Books

http://harrypotter.bloomsbury.com/harrypotter/

Enter through the witches and wizards entrance (of course)! Then give a password
(any name from the book) to pass through a wall. Then you can meet the author,
read about the creation of Harry Potter, get the scoop on the next book, and send a
howler (or an owler if you're nice).

Hogwarts Online

http://library.thinkquest.org/C006090/

This site is a Harry Potter online fan club. It is easy to see that the site creators
love the Harry Potter books. Join them in a wonderful online experience and learn
even more about Harry and all of the book characters.

The Magical World of Harry Potter

http://library.thinkquest.org/J001330/

If you are a Harry Potter fan, you will love this site. Read about Harry, learn about magic, play games, find out about the author, and take a Final Exam.

Mary GrandPré Official Fan Club

http://www.marygrandpre.org/

Read about this award-winning illustrator who is known for her soft geometric style and magical drawings, as well as her work with the Harry Potter books.

Scholastic's Harry Potter

http://www.scholastic.com/harrypotter/home.asp

This sparkling Scholastic site has plenty of fun for young muggles, witches, and wizards. Answer a poll question in the Discussion Chamber, send a quick letter via Owl Post, or test your knowledge in Wizard Trivia (watch out, it's tough!). Have you been tripping over some of the words and names in the Harry Potter books? One of the best parts of this site is the pronunciation guide to help you over those tongue-twisty words. Get a Harry Potter screen saver while you're there!

The Top 50 Harry Potter Sites

http://www.mikids.com/harrypotter

If you are a Harry Potter fanatic, then try this site. You will find the top 50 Harry Potter sites on the web. With all of this Harry Potter information, you are sure to be amused for a long time.

School Stuff
Homework Helpers

Ask an Expert

http://njnie.dl.stevens-tech.edu/askanexpert.html

Are you looking for help in science, math, social studies or English? You're likely to find help here. Just in case you can't find the answer, they have an extensive list of other "Ask an Expert" sites where you are bound to find the right answer.

Awesome Library for Kids

http://www.awesomelibrary.org/student.html

This library site has been divided into two sections: School Subjects, and Fun and More. When using the site, click on a subject or topic area and next find the appropriate grade level. Be sure to check out the "Ask a Question" links.

BigChalk.com

http://www.bigchalk.com

Need homework help? This site claims to be the largest and most helpful homework site online. When you arrive at the site, click on the "students" link. There is more to BigChalk than homework. Play CyberSurfari or other games, contribute to the current poll, and find the latest news. You will not be bored here!

BJ Pinchbeck Homework Helper

http://school.discovery.com/homeworkhelp/bjpinchbeck/

B.J. Pinchbeck and his dad began collecting websites appropriate for kids and decided to share their findings. It was such a success that they teamed up with Discovery School.

Citing Internet Addresses

http://www.classroom.com/resource/citingnetresources.asp

Just as your students need to cite the books and periodicals they use to support their research, so too must they cite online sources of information. This how-to guide from Classroom Connect offers an easy-to-understand method for citing online information in student bibliographies.

Cool Fact of the Day

http://features.LearningKingdom.com/fact/

Learn some interesting fact every day by bookmarking this interesting site. Every day a new fact is posted. It may be science related or it may be some other issue. Some previous facts include: The First Motorcycle, Sonic Boom, Hot Cities, and Quicksand. Subscribe to this site so you don't miss a day.

Graphic Organizers

http://www.sdcoe.k12.ca.us/score/actbank/sorganiz.htm

Need help getting organized? There are a variety of graphic organizers available at this site which can get you started. Some are good for outlining ideas, while others are appropriate for brainstorming. Look at them all and see which ones will work best for you. You might want to share this site with your teacher and get some points!

Harcourt Learning Site

http://www.harcourtschool.com/

Harcourt Brace has set up this site to complement their textbook series. However, there are fun learning activities and games for all. For instance, if you need help with your math addition skills, go to the Math link, choose Math Advantage, and then click on the second grade link. Here you will see "Addition Surprise." Explore the site to find more of the gems.

HomeworkSpot

http://www.homeworkspot.com/

HomeworkSpot is a great place for a student to get help with homework assignments because this site is so complete. Homework help is broken down by grade level and curriculum topic. There are links to plenty of other web resources. For instance, In the News, while only listing a few topics, gives excellent overviews so kids really understand the history of the event.

International Telementors

http://www.telementor.org

The International Telementoring project, which is sponsored by corporations like Hewlett Packard and Merck Institute, uses experienced professionals to share their experiences and expertise through a mentor partnership with students. Classroom teachers need to set this up, but it has proven to be a valuable resource for our future work-force participants.

The Learning Curve

http://library.thinkquest.org/C005704/

Have you ever wondered how people learn, what allows us to learn, or how we shape our own learning ability? If so, then you've come to the right place! Here you will learn not only the basics behind learning, but also effective learning and teaching techniques, conditions that influence learning ability, and how to maximize your learning potential.

Learning Network Student

http://familyeducation.com/k12/Student/

This site is a great resource for students who want or need some homework help. Additionally, you can find fun activities, polls, games, and a Quiz Lab. Be sure to check out the "Thing of the Day" and the Word Quiz.

Lightspan.com's Homework Zone

http://www.lightspan.com/kids/pages/homewkzone/hw.asp?_prod =LS&_nav=k2_HomeworkZone

This site is made up of several components. You can get help with specific assignments, link to helpful sites, bone-up on learning strategies, and more. Be sure to go to the "Favorite Five."

Lightspan.com Kids

http://www.lightspan.com/kids/pages/default.asp?_prod=LS&_nav=k1

Lightspan.com, a well-respected educational site has created a special section just for kids to use. You'll find games, voting, current events, and plenty more great stuff. If you are a parent or teacher, you might want to become a member (it's free) to receive updates on their activities.

Lit Cafe

http://library.thinkquest.org/17500/

This well-executed, excellent site provides basic biographies of some of the most influential writers of the western world, a guide to literary terms and devices (with examples), grammar, roots of words back to the Latin and Greek, English fundamentals, including spelling, and literary devices. This is an enormously helpful resource!

NoodleBib 2.0 (A Free Online Bibliography Maker)

http://www.noodletools.com/

You are getting ready to write a paper and you don't know how to write up the references you are using. This free online program will help you to do that. All you have to do is click on NoodleBib and select the reference type from the pull-down menu.

NoodleQuest 1.0

http://www.noodletools.com/

One of the hardest parts about doing academic research on the Internet is figuring out where to start! A search engine is usually the first thing to try, but what search engines are the most useful for your topic? Fill in a short form, and this site will point you in the right direction.

Pitsco's Ask an Expert

http://www.askanexpert.com/

When you have a question and you don't know where to turn to find the answer, this site may just be the place to start. It offers "hundreds of real world experts" who voluntarily will answer questions for students. Students can either find an expert by category or through a key word search.

SchoolWork.Ugh!

http://www.schoolwork.org

Need help with a homework assignment? Try this site. At the top of the home page you can do a search of the site for your topic, or you can scroll down the page and find a subject area. This site is geared for grade 7+.

Smart Stuff

http://familyeducation.com/channel/0,2916,47,00.html

If you are looking for some fun activities that offer learning opportunities, check out this site. You will find the usual stuff—math, reading, science, geography and history—but they have added in Art Stuff, Music Stuff, Stuff Stuff, and Zine Zone.

StudyWeb

http://www.studyweb.com/

There is something for everyone at this site. Do you want to find out about sports? How about photography or finding a scholarship? You will find 31 categories and endless subcategories.

Test-Taking Tips from the Teacher

http://familyeducation.com/article/0,1120,3-553,00.html

How are you at taking tests? Could you use a few pointers to make the experience a little less stressful? Try this site to gain some helpful tips to make test-taking a happier experience.

The Virtual Reference Desk

http://granite.syr.edu/vrd/

This site can help you find information and answers to your questions about school subjects, fascinating facts, research topics, and more! Connect with experts by using the AskA tabs in the Learning Center. Use the tabs for FAQs, archived questions (previously asked questions), and top sites to find resources selected by librarians and subject area specialists.

Yahoo! WebRings

http://dir.webring.yahoo.com/rw

If you have a particular interest and want to find other similar sites, search here. You can even list your webpage—if it fits into one of the categories—to increase your traffic. Just type in "Kids" and you will find more than 550 sites. Add another word—for instance, "bikes"—and narrow the search to a more manageable "3."

School Stuff
Reference Sites

Allwords.com

http://www.allwords.com/

This word site is one of the most useful sites on the web. In addition to the typical dictionary and thesaurus, you will find writing and language tools along with the ability to translate. But that's not all! There are games and crosswords, too.

Almanacs

http://ln.infoplease.com/almanacs.html

This site contains information on the world, the United States, history and government, biography, sports, entertainment, business and finance, society and culture, health and science, and weather. Within each category there are even more information links.

Biographical Dictionary

http://www.s9.com/biography/

Do you need a quick summary of a significant person? This dictionary covers more than 28,000 notable men and women who have shaped our world from ancient times to the present day.

Dictionary

http://ln.infoplease.com/dictionary.html

This 125,000-word dictionary is sure to have the word you want. In addition, you will find activities for word lovers—crossword puzzles, foreign words and phrases, and a Daily Word Quiz to help you expand your vocabulary.

Dictionary.com

http://dictionary.com/

Need we say more? Look up any troublesome word right here. Also links to Roget's Thesaurus, writing resources, and more.

Encarta

http://encarta.msn.com/

Encarta is one of the all-purpose reference sites. You name it and you will more than likely find something about it here. If you click on reference, you will be able to submit a word for searching on the reference page, or you can scroll down to do a category search. Be sure to try the Homework link.

Encyclopedia

http://ln.infoplease.com/encyclopedia.html

This encyclopedia site allows you to search by key words in the more than 57,000 articles of the Columbia Encyclopedia. It is a breeze to use!

Encyclopedia Britannica

http://www.britannica.com/

The full text of the *Encyclopædia Britannica* has been made available free of charge on the Internet. *Britannica.com* features the Britannica database, original commentary, engaging, and timely multimedia presentations, relevant articles from respected publishers, news, weather, stock quotes, and more—all provided with the authority and expertise of Britannica.

Encyclopedia.com

http://www.encyclopedia.com/

This encyclopedia site is easy to use. Their information is very straightforward. They encourage the searcher to use the cross-references if more in-depth information is needed. In addition to the usual encyclopedia search, use the links at the top of the screen for other reference sources.

Encyclopedia Smithsonian

http://www.si.cdu/rcsource/faq/start.htm

Encyclopedia Smithsonian features answers to frequently asked questions about the Smithsonian and links to Smithsonian resources on subjects from Art to Zoology. This truly is an amazing resource.

Fact Monster - Online Dictionary, Encyclopedia and Homework help

http://www.factmonster.com/

Wow, what an information-rich site! Besides the usual math, science, news, and word stuff, you will find plenty more information. Look at Today in History, take the Monster Poll, check out the Cool Stuff, and find much, much more.

FunkandWagnalls.com

http://www.funkandwagnalls.com

This is a consolidated resource made up of an encyclopedia, dictionary, thesaurus, world atlas, and more rolled into one site. This might be a good first-place to begin a subject search because there is so much information available.

Learn2.com

http://www.learn2.com

Learn2.com is a highly awarded site that features online lessons in hundreds of topics, from cleaning a stereo to learning French and Spanish. Categories include Food and Drink, Healthier Living, Hobbies, Communication, Finance, Childcare, Cleaning, Computers, and Automotive.

Quote of the Day

http://features.learningkingdom.com/quote/

A word topic is chosen for each day and several related quotes from people of stature are posted. Don't miss a day of insightful knowledge—subscribe to this site. Check the archive for other quotes—use the random button for a surprise quote.

Thesaurus.com

http://www.thesaurus.com/

This is a Thesaurus site and more. If you want to use the Thesaurus, you can find words by headword or category. You also have access to a dictionary, periodicals, crossword puzzles, translator, and so much more. Sign up for the "Word for the Day" to increase your vocabulary.

Yahoo Encyclopedia List

http://dir.yahoo.com/reference/encyclopedia/

If you have exhausted all of your encyclopedias and you need another, then try this Yahoo site. There are some fairly unusual ones listed along with Britannica and Columbia Encyclopedia.

Science

BrainPOP

http://www.brainpop.com/

BrainPOP's motto is "the more you know, the more you know" and that is why they offer so many opportunities to learn about health, science, and technology through movies. Use the pull-down menu to select a movie. Get the popcorn ready. Be sure to read the text below the movie as it plays.

Bridges

http://www.pbs.org/wgbh/buildingbig/bridge/index.html

There are more than half a million bridges in the United States, and you rely on them every day to cross obstacles like streams, valleys, and railroad tracks. But do you know how they work? Or why some bridges are curved while others are straight? Find the answers and much more about bridges at this physics site.

Dams

http://www.pbs.org/wgbh/buildingbig/dam/index.html

With the exception of the Great Wall of China, dams are the largest structures ever built. Throughout history, big dams have prevented flooding, irrigated farmland, and generated tremendous amounts of electricity. Without dams, modern life as we know it would simply not be the same. Find out more about dams at this site.

Domes

http://www.pbs.org/wgbh/buildingbig/dome/index.html

They have been called "the kings of all roofs," and they cover some of our most important buildings. Domes are curved structures—they have no angles and no corners—and they enclose an enormous amount of space without the help of a single column. Despite their thinness, domes are some of the strongest and stiffest structures in existence today. This site has an abundance of information on domes.

DragonFly

http://www.muohio.edu/dragonfly/

Feeling bored? Not any more—that is if you visit this site. Science topics found here include navigation, space, time, water, people and plants, small and tall, earth sounds, using tools, trees and seeds, and more.

Explore Zone

http://explorezone.com/

This incredible site has the most up-to-date information on things that are happening to our planet and beyond. If you want to know the latest—space, earthquake, Mission launches, weather, tides, volcanoes, and more—you must visit the Zone.

Federal Railroad Administration Kids' Site

http://www.fra.dot.gov/s/edu/

The Federal Railroad Administration designed this site to educate students about railroads. Kids can learn about railroad safety, get information on trains and careers in the railroad industry, and view video clips.

Field Tips for Field Trips

http://www.childrensmuseum.org/geomysteries/fieldtrips.html

Going into the field in search of rocks, minerals, and fossils is a lot of fun. At this site you will find some tips to make your experience even better.

Find Out Why

http://www.findoutwhy.org/

Find Out Why is made up of several pages. One is Find Out More, which answers questions like, "Why does the wind blow?" or "Why is there lightening?" There are other activities—games and animations—which go along with the questions.

Fun for Scienz Kids

http://members.aol.com/ScienzFair/fun.htm

Here are some fun science experiments for kids to do at home. Have a blast as you make bubbles, paper airplanes, and more. Kids, be sure to check with your parents before you try these ideas.

Gizmo of the Week

http://features.learningkingdom.com/gizmo/

Did you ever wonder how a steam engine works? Or, how about a VCR? Check this site out to find the answers. If you don't want to miss a week, subscribe to the site. Appropriate for grades 7+.

Hoover Dam

http://www.pbs.org/wgbh/amex

When you arrive at this site use the pull-down menu to find Hoover Dam. The left sidebar menu allows you to navigate through the special features, maps, timelines, and the people and events related to the topic.

How Stuff Works

http://www.howstuffworks.com/

Have you ever wondered how a clock works, how a DVD player plays a movie, or how a cassette tape can record sound? Visit this site and you will find the answer to these questions and many more.

Kids' Castle Science

http://www.kidscastle.si.edu/

If you like science, enter this site and click on the scientist. There is a message board where questions are posed and readers can respond. You can learn about Morse's telegraph, quartz amethyst, sunspots, and more. Be sure to read the feature articles too.

Imagine the Universe

http://imagine.gsfc.nasa.gov/docs/homepage.html

This site is intended for students age 14 and up, and for anyone interested in learning about our universe. This site will give young people a glimpse into the mysteries of our universe, what we know about it, how it is evolving, and the kinds of objects it contains. This site is in an e-zine format and contains a lot of information.

Internet Fairgrounds

http://library.thinkquest.org/C002926

Here is your chance to learn about a fairground—it's history, how it works, the rides, how they make money, and what safety precautions are involved.

The Laboratory

http://www.funology.com/laboratory/index.cfm

If you like to perform science experiments, the Laboratory has a ton of them that will keep you busy. Click on one of the categories (Physics, Chemistry, Biology, or Weather) to choose what experiments you want to try first.

Scholastic's The Magic School Bus

http://www.scholastic.com/magicschoolbus/index.htm

Things always get more interesting when Ms. Frizzle is around. Visit the Activity Lab to launch FrizTV for some fresh facts, create monster bugs, chomp your way through a maze, and much more. Who knew learning could be so much fun?

The Museum of Innovation

http://www.thetech.org/

The tech "hands on-line" interactive museum explores the technology and science, which is changing the world in which we live. Some of the exhibits include robotics, earthquakes, "Make a Splash with Color," and more.

National Inventors Hall of Fame

http://www.invent.org/

Would you like to find out about inventions? This website has information about inventors and inventions. It also supplies information on what to do when you want to patent an invention of your own.

NOAA Photo Library

http://www.photolib.noaa.gov/

On any given day NOAA personnel could be chasing tornadoes, flying into hurricanes, battling stormy seas, tagging turtles and whales, taking scientific readings at the South Pole, monitoring the health of coral reefs, or engaging in virtually any task related to monitoring our environment and the health of our planet. This site presents the photographs that are a result of their monitoring efforts.

The Royal Observatory Greenwich

http://www.rog.nmm.ac.uk/

The Royal Observatory Greenwich is part of the National Maritime Museum and home of the Prime Meridian of the world. Visit this site to learn about time (e.g., there is a map that shows the area of the world covered by darkness and light), seasons, the calendar and much, much more.

Science Education Gateway (SEGway)

http://cse.ssl.berkeley.edu/SEGway/

Try a self-guided science lesson and learn more about space and astronomy. Choose an interview to hear what solar scientists have to say about the sun. Find out about the latest astronomical news and events. Follow an on-line NASA Quest "chat" between youngsters and an astronomer. What you can learn at SEGway today? Click on the "For the Public" button to proceed.

Science Rock

http://genxtvland.simplenet.com/SchoolHouseRock/science.hts?hi

Remember these songs? Your kids will love them too! Songs/subjects include: "Interplant Janet—The Solar System," "Telegraph Line—The Central Nervous System," "Them Not-So-Dry Bones—All about the Skeleton," and more.

ScienzFair Project Ideas

http://members.aol.com/ScienzFair/ideas.htm

Looking for a science fair project idea? If you visit this site you will know you are in the right place to find an idea. There are more than 20 subject categories from which to look. Additionally, you will find a links to other sites, tips, and more.

Seismology at the Science Fair

http://ncweb-north.wr.usgs.gov/info/scifair/

Are you interested in earthquakes as a science fair topic? Turn to this site as you begin your study; there are links to valuable resources such as completed science fair projects on the topic, how to build a seismometer, geology activities for all ages, and much more.

Skyscrapers

http://www.pbs.org/wgbh/buildingbig/skyscraper/index.html

The term "skyscraper" was coined in the 1880s, shortly after the first tall buildings were constructed in the United States, but the history of tall buildings dates back hundreds of years. Since the Middle Ages, engineers have engaged in a battle for the sky. Learn about skyscrapers at this information-rich site.

Tunnels

http://www.pbs.org/wgbh/buildingbig/tunnel/index.html

Tunnels provide some of the last available space for cars and trains, water and sewage, even power and communication lines. Today, it's safe to bore through mountains and burrow beneath oceans — but it was not always this way. In fact, it took engineers thousands of years to perfect the art of digging tunnels. Find out about tunnel construction and more at this packed-with-information resource.

What in the World Could It Be?

http://www.ars.usda.gov/is/kids/microscope/microscope.htm

Have some fun and test your ability to reason. At this site you will see a magnified picture of an item and you must determine what it is. Have fun as you use reasoning skills to choose one of three answers.

The Why Files

http://whyfiles.org/

The Why Files cover issues of science, health, environment, and technology from a unique perspective. Using news and current events as a springboard to explore science and the larger issues it raises, they hope to show science as a human enterprise and a way of looking at the world. Beyond portraying the outcomes of science, their overarching goal is to explain the process, culture and people that shape it. Check out the archives for past articles.

The Yuckiest Site on the Internet

http://yucky.kids.discovery.com/

First there was mud. Then there were worms. And now there is Yucky! Test your skills with Whack-A-Roach. All you need to know about barfing, belching, and blackheads! Plus mad scientist fun in Yucky Labs!

Zoom Inventors and Inventions

http://www.enchantedlearning.com/inventors/

This Invention site is great for the researcher. If you know the name of a specific inventor, you can look him or her up alphabetically. Or, you can look for the region of the world or the era in which the object was invented. Maybe you will be inspired to come up with an invention of your own.

Space

Amazing Space Web-Based Activities

http://amazing-space.stsci.edu/

Amazing Space is a set of web-based activities primarily designed for classroom use, but made available for all to enjoy. Be brave and take the Astronaut Challenge, find out the truth about Black Holes, or sign up for the Hubble Deep Field Academy. And there is plenty more to try.

Astronomy Cafe

http://itss.raytheon.com/cafe/qadir/qanda.html

Do you like learning about space? If so, make sure you visit this site where answers have been posted to over 3000 questions. Subjects include: Black Holes, Satellites, the Planets, Strange Sightings, and Science Fair Projects. This is only the beginning!

Be a Spacecraft Engineer

http://stardust.jpl.nasa.gov/education/jason/index2.html

NASA needs your help! As part of an international coalition, it has begun building the International Space Station. But the Space Station is threatened by orbital debris: abandoned satellites, rocket remnants, and many other things. Can you design a spacecraft to protect the Space Station from this "space junk"?

The Best of the Hubble Space Telescope

http://www.seds.org/hst/hst.html

If you are looking for images of space, then you should try this site. The images on this site are from the Hubble Space Telescope. They are always updating the links so there are fresh images.

CosmicQuest

http://www.childrensmuseum.org/cosmicquest/

Visit the CosmicQuest site and you will find: Living in Space: Design a Space Station; Field Guide to the Universe; Expedition to the North Magnetic Pole; and SpaceWatch Webcasts.

JSC Kids Shortcuts

http://www.jsc.nasa.gov/pao/students

This site contains references to other Internet space sites. For example, you will find the following links: International Space Station, The Search for Life on Mars, From Earth to Eros. There are more than 25 links.

Kids' Castle Air and Space

http://www.kidscastle.si.edu/channels/air-space/air-space.html

If you like air travel and space, don't miss this site. There is a message board where questions are posted and readers can respond. You can learn about the Spirit of St. Louis, Space Shuttle Enterprise, Solar Eclipses, and more. Be sure to read the feature articles, too.

Kodak

http://www.kodak.com/

Did you know that the Kodak Company was involved in space imaging? Go to the Kodak site and use the Site Directory pull-down menu to find Space Imaging. Read about Kodak involvement with NASA's Mars Rover, Chandra X-ray Observatory, and more.

NASA KIDS

http://kids.msfc.nasa.gov/

Would-be astronauts should visit this site for some serious space exploration. Try the puzzles, figure out how old you would be in space, participate in online learning activities, read space stories, and visit the Art Gallery.

NASA Quest

http://quest.arc.nasa.gov/interactive/hst.html/index.html

Realizing the power of the Internet, NASA Quest was set up so that NASA scientists could bring their knowledge to students and classrooms. Through this website learn about the Space Team, the Aerospace Team, the Solar System, and Deep Space. Stop by the Kid's Corner to see the work of your peers.

NASA Space and Beyond

http://kids.msfc.nasa.gov/Space/

Check out this site to learn where the space station is and how it functions. In order to survive, people need clean air and water. This site explains the process of providing that in space. There are other great links about the earth, moon, quasars, stars, etc. that should not be missed.

The Nine Planets: A Multimedia Tour of the Solar System

http://seds.lpl.arizona.edu/billa/tnp/

The Nine Planets is an overview of the history, mythology, and current scientific knowledge of each of the planets and moons in our solar system. Each page has text and images, some have sounds and movies, and most provide references to additional related information.

Puzzles (and other activities)

http://kids.msfc.nasa.gov/Puzzles/

Have some fun as you learn about space. NASA has created this site with many learning activities. Try the puzzles, figure out how old you would be in space, participate in some of the online learning activities, read the space stories, and visit the Art Gallery.

Rockets

http://kids.msfc.nasa.gov/Rockets/

The Space Shuttle, Airplanes, Satellites, Space Probes, Rocket Detector, Apollo 11, Launching from a Spinning Planet, Mapping Earth from Space, and Space Team Online are the topics of this site. Be sure to look at All about Rockets— Documents to download.

The Space Place

http://spaceplace.jpl.nasa.gov/spacepl.htm

This nifty site encourages kids to learn about space. Try "Make Spacey Things" where students make a "Galactic Mobile" or "Blame It on El Niño Pudding." In "Do Spacey Things" students can try "Get a Space Nose" or "Fall Into a Black Hole."

Spaceviews: Mars Pathfinder

http://www.seds.org/spaceviews/pathfinder/

This publication, owned by SPACE.com, covers recent developments in space policy, exploration, development, and more. Learn about recent space launches and upcoming events, political developments, cutting-edge research in new space-related technologies, and other areas. This Website is updated on a daily basis with the latest space news.

StarChild: A Learning Center for Young Astronomers

http://starchild.gsfc.nasa.gov/docs/StarChild/StarChild.html

Have you thought about becoming an astronaut? Would you like to learn more about space? Well, this site is just what you need. It is written at two levels: Level 1 for younger children and Level 2 for older students. Topics include the solar system, universe, space stuff, and the glossary.

What is the Aurora?

http://www.pfrr.alaska.edu/~ddr/ASGP/STRSCOOP/AURORA/INDEX.HTM

The aurora borealis has fascinated, and often terrified, humans for thousands of years. The people of the north who saw the aurora frequently developed many legends and stories about it, while those who lived further south and rarely saw the aurora thought it was a supernatural omen of war or destruction. Find out what the aurora really is at this site.

Who's Out There? A Space Science Adventure

http://www.seti.org/game/index.html

Who's out there? Are humans alone in the universe? Scientists involved in SETI   the Search for Extraterrestrial Intelligence—are using modern technology to search for the answer to this age-old question. What if you were hired to lead such a search? Explore what you need to know to design a SETI research project, then test your skills at searching for alien signals!

Zoom Astronomy

http://www.EnchantedLearning.com/subjects/astronomy/

Zoom Astronomy is a comprehensive on-line site about space and astronomy. It is designed for people of all ages and levels of comprehension. It has an easy-to-use structure that allows readers to start at a basic level on each topic and then progress to much more advanced information as desired, simply by clicking on links.

Sports
General

CNN Sports Illustrated

http://sportsillustrated.cnn.com/scoreboards/index.html

Get the latest sport scores from this site. Not only can you get today's scores, but you also can pick up the scores from the previous days. College information is included on this site too.

College Sports News Daily

http://www.collegesportsnews.com/

If college sports are your interest, you will enjoy this collegiate site. Baseball, basketball, football, soccer, and volleyball are some of the sports that are covered here. Check the additional links in the side-bars.

International Olympic Committee

http://www.olympic.org/

The International Olympic Committee created this website to provide current information about the organization and the Olympic events. In addition to information about the International Olympic Committees and the Olympic Museum, you can find information on the three upcoming Olympic host cities. Make sure you look at the TV clips of past events.

Kids' Castle - Sports

http://www.kidscastle.si.edu/channels/sports/sports.html

If you like sports, you will want to visit this site. There is a message board where questions are posed and readers can respond. You can learn about climbing walls, rowing, swimming the channel, and more. Be sure to read the feature articles, too.

Safety on Wheels

http://www.choa.org/safety/wheels/

It is recommended that children wear safety gear when participating in any kind of wheel sport. This site has tips on how to buy and use safety helmets needed for these sports. Also, there are Tips on bicycles, skateboards, and in-line skates for free-wheeling Kids.

Small Motor Skills

http://www.familyplay.com/activities/actSmallmotor.html

This site has many activities for small children that concentrate on the small motor skills like eye-hand coordination, hand and finger movement, balance, and more.

Special Olympics

http://www.specialolympics.org/about_special_olympics/index.html

Special Olympics is an international program of year-round sports training and athletic competition for more than one million children and adults with mental retardation. This site offers information on the various activities of this organization and how volunteers can get involved.

Sports Illustrated for Kids

http://www.sikids.com/

This site is a must-see for all of you sport lovers. Here you will find the latest information on your favorite teams and players. Take a look at the Birthday Finders to see which athletes share your birthday, try the Sports Trivia to see how much you really know, and vote for the Athlete of the Week. But don't stop there, check out the other great stuff.

Sports Scholarships and Academic Sports Scholarships

http://www.academic-sports.com/default.htm

Are you interested in getting a sports scholarship or academic sports scholarship? Try this site as a first step in the process. There are two entry points: the Men's Sport Scholarship Network and the Women's Sport Scholarship Network. There is a small fee involved.

SurfMonkey Sports Zone

http://www.surfmonkey.com/fun/sports_zone/default.asp

There are plenty of games and activities on this sports site. Try the links to Bboards, chats, games, fun, and other sites. Best of all, connect with Nirve TV and choose land, water, or snow.

Unusual Sports in the Olympics

http://library.thinkquest.org/J002862/

Everyone has heard of figure skating and gymnastics, but how many people know the thrill of racing down an ice covered track on a sled or the beauty of water ballet? This website explores the unusual sports in the Olympics: the ones that may not get much press attention, but that have dedicated athletes just the same. After visiting this informative and interactive site, you won't see the Olympics in the same light again.

Yahooligans! Sports

http://www.yahooligans.com/content/sports/

Send your budding sports nut to this site for today's scores and top news stories. Short blurbs and trivia from *Sports Illustrated For Kids* are easy for kids to read. The site is set up to be a jump-off page to help kids read more about their favorite sports.

Sports
Auto Racing

Indy Racing

http://www.indyracingleague.com/

Almost everything you want to know about Indy Racing is available at this website. The major events of the season—Indianapolis 500, Brickyard 400, and USGP—are listed here along with other events. (Did you know the PGA plays a big event at the Brickyard?) Other information that you can mine from this site includes cars, drivers, stats, tracks, etc.

NASCAR Online

http://www.nascar.com/

The National Association of Stock Car Auto Racing hosts this site for its fans. Get news, stats, track information, schedules, etc. In the Garage, read about the cars that are racing and modifications that are made to them. Catch up on the latest technology that may eventually make it to a car you buy in the future.

NHRA

http://www.nhra.com/

The National Hot Rod Association created this website for its fans. Get the latest schedule of events. Learn about the latest cars. Get the latest scoop on the drivers or delve into the archive of information.

SCCA

http://www.scca.org/

The Sports Car Club of America is the premiere organization for the amateur sports car racer wannabe. This organization holds racing events, performance and road rallies, and solo (driving skills) events, along with some driving schools. Use the pull-down menus to lead you to the professional SCCA events.

Sports
Baseball

Babe Ruth History

http://www.baberuthmuseum.com/html/display.asp?recno=6

Visit this website and learn how Babe Ruth went from an incorrigible boy to a man with baseball ability—the homerun king—who was the envy of the world.

Exploratorium Science of Baseball

http://www.exploratorium.edu/baseball/

What's the science behind a home run? Why do curveballs curve? Learn the game from players from the S.F. Giants and Oakland A's.

History of the World Series

http://www.sportingnews.com/archives/worldseries/

Are you one of those baseball fans that would never miss the World Series no matter what teams are playing? Well then, this site is just for you. You will find all of the latest World Series action and all of the archived information from previous years.

Jackie Robinson and other Baseball Highlights

http://memory.loc.gov/ammem/jrhtml/jrhome.html

When Jackie Robinson took the field as a Brooklyn Dodger in 1947, he became the first African American to play major league baseball in the twentieth century. This Library of Congress site shares the materials that tell his story, and the history of baseball in general.

Little League Online

http://www.littleleague.org/

Get the latest Little League news, learn to start a new league, read about Little League structure and divisions, find a local league, and more. Plus, there's fun stuff like a Little League photo contest and coverage on the year's Little League World Series.

Learn2 Break in a Baseball Mitt

http://www.learn2.com/04/0436/0436.asp

So you need to learn how to break in a baseball mitt. This site will tell you how to do that. In fact it has 5 different ways that you can break in a special mitt. You will surely find one method that will work for you.

Major League Baseball

http://www.sportsline.com/u/baseball/mlb/index.html

This major league baseball site offers quick stats on standings, schedules, teams, and players. Additionally, you can read the latest baseball news stories. Make sure you try the multimedia links.

National Baseball Hall of Fame and Museum

http://baseballhalloffame.org/

National Baseball Hall of Fame and Museum is a much loved and respected organization. Of course you will want to see who is a member of the National Baseball Hall of Fame, but don't miss the Exhibits and Collections, or the Research Library. Try the games, too!

Negro Baseball League

http://www.blackbaseball.com/

Did you know that there was a special baseball league for black players? Visit this website to read the history of this league, discover who the players were, and why the league no longer exists.

The Official Online Community of Ponyball and Softball

http://www.pony.org/mytp/home/pbsn_index.jsp

PONY Baseball and Softball is a community-based sports organization, founded in Washington, Pennsylvania, in 1951. It now has more than 400,000 members from ages 5 through 18 participating in the United States and over 20 nations around the world. Check this site out for more information on leagues near you.

Sports in Space

http://www.muohio.edu/dragonfly/sports/

If you were on Mars or Pluto, how hard would you have to hit a baseball to get a home run? Start on Earth and find out about the rest of the planets at this site. Play Ball!

Total Baseball

http://www.totalbaseball.com/

If you want to know about baseball, this site is just what you need. You can catch up-to-the-minute news about schedules, game results, players, trades, and a whole lot more. Check often as this site is updated daily.

Sports
Basketball

Basketball Explorations

http://library.thinkquest.org/12006/

Basketball is a game that involves several disciplines including math, physics, and art. This site attempts to show you the connections by looking at topics like the geometry of a basketball court, team logos, color theory, and game statistics. Finish up with a final exam and the Color Picker game.

Basketball Locker Room

http://library.thinkquest.org/J002516F/

Enter The Basketball Locker Room to learn about the history of basketball, the greatest players and coaches, and different ways to play basketball. When you finish looking through the site, you can take a quiz or play a hangman game to see if you remember what you read.

Michael Jordan

http://jordan.sportsline.com/

Michael Jordan, the great all-round athlete, has a homepage for his fans. Visit this site to get the latest news on Jordan, and to revisit his glorious career through video clips. You can chat with others about this star and play games.

National Basketball Association (NBA)

http://www.nba.com/

Catch the latest basketball news at this site. Additionally, you will find stats, schedules, history, chats, and information about teams, players, global basketball, and tickets.

NCAA Basketball

http://www.ncaabasketball.net/

Follow Division I men's and women's basketball scores as they happen, order tickets, vote in a basketball poll, and get the top news stories. Everything you need to know about college basketball is here—bring on March Madness!

Shaquille O'Neal

http://www.shaq.com/

Shaq has his own website for his fans. You can find his schedule of games and appearances, get playoff stats, view photos, and listen to audio clips. Don't miss "Match Shaq" a game in the Fun Center.

The Turner Sports WebCam

http://sportsillustrated.cnn.com/turnersports/webcam/

Turner Sports brings you the best seat in the house for every NBA game, when you log in to a bird's eye view of the NBA on TNT and TBS studio show. After the game, stay connected for "INSIDE the NBA," when the live eye turns to the virtual studio, giving you an exclusive preview of the latest in broadcast technology.

Women's National Basketball Association (WNBA)

http://www.wnba.com/

Are you interested in basketball either as a spectator or participant? Check out his site of the WNBA. You can learn about teams, players, coaches, schedules, and more. Try the Sights and Sounds where you can watch a video clip from a recent game.

Sports
Bicycling

Bicycling Magazine

http://www.bicyclingmagazine.com/

If you want or need the most up-to-date information on bicycling, come to this site. What's your interest? Mountain biking? Touring? All the information that you need is here. If you are a true enthusiast you might want to set this as your portal page to the WWW.

The WWW Bicycle Repair Shop

http://www.bicyclerepairshop.com

While this bicycle repair site isn't huge, it does offer basic information on how to repair a bicycle. When you arrive at the site, note the window on the left side of the scene. Choose if you want to repair a mountain or touring bike, then click on the area of the bike that you need.

Propelled by Pedals: A Fun Guide to Bicycles

http://library.thinkquest.org/J002670/

Are you getting ready to buy a bike? Do you know how to buy a bike? Propelled by Pedals website presents the information you need when making a bicycle purchase and you can have a great time while you are learning. This is a must-see site!

Société du Tour de France

http://www.letour.fr/

This is the official website of the famous Le Tour de France. Information of previous races is available at this site. You can see the upcoming year's race route and find more specific information concerning entrants. Notice that the site is offered both in French and English.

Sports
Climbling

All Things Everest

http://climb.mountainzone.com/everest/html/index.html

Would you like to read about the yearly treks to Nepal and the attempted climbs—some successful and some tragically not—of this highest peak in the world? This site contains much information about the climbers of Mt. Everest and their journeys. Reading the information provided here will make you feel like you are a member of a climbing team.

Crown of Africa: Unlocking the Secrets of Mt. Kilimanjaro

http://www.altrec.com/features/

Have you ever thought about climbing a mountain? At the entry page of this site, scroll down to and click on Crown of Africa. Here you will gain an idea of the process one goes through to climb a mountain—from the training you need to do in advance, getting the necessary gear, to studying the geography of the mountain, and more.

Going Up? Get Fit

http://www.exploratorium.edu/sports/goingup/index.html

The 18,000-foot Mt. Parinacota presents some fitness challenges for climbers. Check this article from the Exploratorium Magazine.

Mt. Everest: Crown of the World

http://tqjunior.thinkquest.org/5069/

This interesting site made by students details information about Mt. Everest. Not only will you find geographical information, but you also will be able to read about its history, the climbers, tragedies on the mountain, and more. Don't miss the games.

Sports
Fitness

4-Week Fitness Challenge

http://jfg.girlscouts.org/Go/Fitness/challenge/week1.htm#Week 1: Get Moving:

Would you like a fitness challenge? Try this site. The Girl Scouts created a reasonable 4-week challenge, which includes walking or running along with exercises. They gently get you moving, working up to a more rigorous 4th week.

It's Time to Exercise

http://www.kidshealth.org/kid/stay_healthy/fit/what_time.html

Whatever is going on, as long as you've got a body, it's always the right time to exercise! You don't need fancy equipment or expensive sneakers. You don't need a ton of kids around. Sometimes you don't even need to leave the house to get exercise. Turn to this site for ways to exercise—some ordinary, some innovative.

RaceWalk.com

http://www.racewalk.com/

Racewalk.com, the official race walking home page of USATF, provides all the information you need to start and improve your walking program (whether for competition or fitness) and increase your awareness of other events in the walking community.

Turnstep.com

http://www.turnstep.com/

Are you into aerobics? Try this site for information on routines, music, and video reviews. There is a huge database of patterns or routines so you are bound to find something that you like. There is a bulletin board for posting question or comments.

Sports
Football

ESPN Football

http://football.espn.go.com/nfl/index

From the NFL to the College League, you will find all of your football news on this site. Some of the news includes scores, standings, statistics, transactions, injuries, and players.

NFL.com

http://www.nfl.com/

Connect to the official web page of your favorite team by clicking on their symbol on the top of the page. Get NFL news from the beginning of the season to the Superbowl. You'll find schedules, games, film, polls, and more here.

Play Football - The Official NFL Site for Kids

http://www.playfootball.com/

This site designed for young football fans has football facts, message boards, games (like Tackleman), contests, and tips on playing and watching football.

XFL.com

http://www.xfl.com/

It's the latest league in football, and if you're a football fan, you'll want to keep an eye on it. Get info on the teams behind the scenes and on the field right here.

Sports
Golf

GolfOnline

http://www.golfonline.com/

Golf Magazine has created this website for golf fans. At this site you can find the latest golf scores and stats, schedule for golf events, information on some of the golfers, rules, and news. There are links to some of the golf associations, too.

Ladies Professional Golf Association

http://www.lpga.com/

Are you interested in golf? This complete site offers information on the players, scores, calendar of events, and gives a Tip of the Week. Be sure to click on the Junior Golfer link for information that relates to young girls.

PGA.com Junior Golf Center

http://www.pga.org/juniors/index.html

This site is just for kids. Here you will find etiquette, rules, and a Cool Kids Quiz. For extra information read the Junior Journal. The PGA also sponsors Clubs for Kids, an equipment source for kids who cannot afford clubs.

Teaching Kids Golf

http://www.teachkidsgolf.com/

Want to learn how to play golf? Visit this website where you can watch streaming video and learn the fundamentals of golf, improve your skills, and have fun. When you finish this online tutorial, you will be on your way to having a life-long form of exercise and entertainment.

Sports
Hockey

How Hockey Works

http://www.interlog.com/~tf/howhockeyworks.html

This site contains several articles about the ins and outs of hockey. For instance, you can read "Mask Mastery: Perfecting the Form Took Cagey Thinking" or "Recipe in Rubber: How Discs Get Done Like Dinner."

The Junior Hockey News

http://www.tjhn.com/home.html

This magazine site's purpose is to provide hockey news and information to junior hockey players (ages 19 and under and school, club, or midget teams). You can subscribe to the print magazine, chat, and use the links for games, team information, or sponsors.

National Hockey League

http://www.nhl.com/

So you can't get to the TV but you want to know what's happening at the hockey game? Try your computer! You can listen to a game using RealAudio. Check out the schedule posted online and tune in…well, click in. Plenty of other hockey information is available at this site.

Science of Hockey

http://www.exploratorium.edu/hockey/index.html

The Science of Hockey is the first in a series of "Sports Science" resources developed by the Exploratorium. This site takes you inside the game: you'll hear from NHL players and coaches from the San Jose Sharks, as well as leading physicists and chemists.

Sports
In-Line Skating

International Inline Skating Association

http://www.iisa.org/

The International Inline Skating Association was founded to promote inline skating. In accord with this goal, the association develops instructional material and promotes safe skating. Additionally, skating lessons, information on how to purchase skates, and schedules of events are posted here.

Rollerblade

http://www.rollerblade.com/

Whether you are the novice just learning how to rollerblade or the expert, you will enjoy this site. Get the low down on equipment, safety issues, fitness, and more at this site. Don't miss the skate scenes: Fitness and Aggressive.

Roller Hockey

http://www.rhockey.com/

Welcome to Roller Hockey Online, where they serve up the hottest roller action on the web. Get the latest info on new gear, playing tips, pro coverage, news, events, plus lots more. Stay in the game with this site's help.

Skating FAQs

http://www.skatefaq.com/

Every question that you have about inline skating is probably answered at this site. To begin with, you will find general information about the sport and specific information on techniques. There is a tutorial as well as equipment information.

Sports
Jump Rope

iJump rope

http://freestyle-jumproping.com/

Would you like free jump rope lessons? This site offers just that, and they are interactive. You can view the film clips as QuickTime or Flash. But don't stop here. Read about the benefits of jumping rope and sign up for the free e-newsletter.

Jump Rope for Heart - Skills

http://www.heartfoundation.com.au/school/jump/skills.html

Want to do some exercise? How about jumping rope? This site shows different jump rope techniques—e.g., bell jump and side saddle jump—to vary the usual routine.

Jump Rope Rhymes

http://www.corpcomm.net/~gnieboer/jumprope.htm

Come to this site if you want to jump rope with some fun in mind. At this site you will find rhymes to say while getting in your exercise. For instance, you will find Coffee & Tea, Doctor Doctor, Down in the Valley, and Found a Peanut.

United States Amateur Jump Rope Federation

http://www.usajrf.org/home.htm

Did you know a jump rope organization even existed? If you enjoy jumping rope, you might want to know that even adults enjoy the activity and that's why this site exists. There are plenty of links to get you to other jump rope sites.

Sports
Skateboarding

Chuck's Skateboard Place

http://www.sapskateboards.com/chuck/htms/ckparks.htm

Chuck has a great skateboard site with loads of information. See how to construct a halfpipe. Look at the photos of skateboarders in action and send in your own. Chuck also has a list of skate parks.

The History of Skateboarding

http://www.discovery.com/stories/history/toys/SKATEBOARD/shoulda.html

Have you heard of sidewalk or terra-surfing? When surfers became bored with the flat surf of the ocean in California, one ingenious man decided to have some fun with skates mounted on a board. Read how this action sparked enthusiasm for the skateboards of today.

Skateboarding.com

http://www.Skateboarding.com/

Visit this site to read about the latest news in skateboarding. This site has feature articles, a buyers guide, product reviews, trick tips, photos, chats, and much more. If you like skate boarding, you will like this site.

Skate Board Science

http://www.exploratorium.edu/skateboarding/

If you are a skate board enthusiast, visit this site. You can watch a webcast and see skateboarding pros—Wade Speyer, Dustin Dollin, Matt Fields, Mikey Reyes, Paul Zuanich, and others. Paul Doherty, Exploratorium staff physicist, explains the physics of ollies, nolies, and kickflips.

Sports
Skiing

Kid Ski

http://www.kid-ski.com/

You are an avid skier and now you would like to give your children the same experience. Go to this site and see the right approach to take. This is a commercial site with a proven method for teaching very young children how to ski.

Skiing.com

http://www.ski.com/

Everything you need to plan a ski vacation is at this site: information on resorts, transportation, ski rental equipment, weather, trail maps, snow accumulation, and more. If you can't get away for a ski vacation now, check the mountain cams for a virtual experience.

SkiNet.com

http://www.skinet.com/

This site is a great resource for snow conditions, travel, gear, resorts, instruction tips, news, and more. Sign up for SkiNet's SkiMail newsletter, a free biweekly email update of what's going on in the world of skiing.

Ski Search

http://www.ski-search.com/sp_db/index.shtml

This ski site has all types of current information about skiing. You will find discussion areas, snow reports, news from the slopes, and ratings of ski resorts. After a skiing vacation, you might want to give your own report on the experience.

Sports
Snowboarding

SnowboarderREVIEW

http://www.snowboarderreview.com/index.shtml

Looking for some new equipment? Find product reviews by boarders for boarders. This site also includes message boards, classifieds, articles, a directory of resorts, a list of heli/snowcat tour operators, and more.

Snowboarding.com

http://www.snowboarding.com/

Snowboarding.com has all the gear a boarder might want, plus a photo gallery, news, product reviews, and more. See the favorite tricks posted with How To's and a terms dictionary. And, find out about snowboarding events, like the Chevy Truck US Snowboard Gran Prix and the Vans Triple Crown of Snowboarding.

SnowboardingOnline.com

http://www.twsnow.com/

Here is a site that contains information on snowboarding. In addition to the News, Photos, and Chat, check on the Equipment, Instruction, Weather, and Competition section of the website. Click on Profiles to read about people in the sport.

Snowboard Online Television

http://soltv.com/

Check out this archive of video clips and downloads of snowboarding action. Also find links to all kinds of cool snowboarding sites.

Sports
Soccer

ATL World Cup Soccer

http://www.wldcup.com/

Get today's World Cup soccer news from around the world at this site. In addition to the news, you can get player and country profiles, the schedule of events, chat, and match results. If you want to keep up with the most current information, subscribe to the free email news.

American Youth Soccer Organization

http://www.soccer.org/

AYSO's goal is to provide children a safe and organized soccer team experience. It believes in a fun and family environment and promotes everyone plays, balanced teams, open registration, positive coaching, and good sportsmanship. This site has the latest info on signing up, locations, coaches, etc.

UEFA.org

http://www.uefa.org

This site is dedicated to the European Football Association, commonly known as soccer in America. Get the latest information on the sport as it is seen through the eyes of the Europeans. Here you will find information on its club leagues, women's and men's teams, as well as their youth teams.

Women's Soccer World Magazine

http://www.womensoccer.com/

This magazine is devoted soley to women's soccer. Click on Girls Soccer World to find information on girls' teams, training tips, college teams, and camps.

Sports
Surfing

Legendary Surfers

http://www.legendarysurfers.com/

Okay surfers, get some great background information on legendary surfers and what made them so. In addition to information on surfers like Kahanamoku, Bob Simmons, and Buzzy Trent, there is information on boards, the origin of surfing, etc.

National Scholastic Surfing Association (NSSA)

http://www.nssa.org/

This website is for anyone who is interested in the sports of surfing and bodyboarding. They have organized the National Scholastic Surfing Association into categories on the left side of the page so you can jump easily into areas of interest. Many areas of the site will be updated on a regular basis.

Swell

http://www.swell.com/sw/content/home_flash.jsp

Get the news on Swell Surfline, visit the Surfshop for gear, take a look at the travel coverage on the best surfing spots, and more.

WorldSurfers e-Mag

http://www.worldsurfers.com/

Check out online surf videos, read recent and past Worldsurfers stories, find out competition winners announced, get the history of surfing, and link to personal websites of surfers. Don't miss the cameras section that links to great surf cams worldwide.

Sports
Swimming & Water Polo

Swimmersworld.com

http://www.swimmersworld.com/

The leading website for competitive swimming news and information, you'll find meet results, recruiting, club pages, and more at Swimmersworld.com.

Synchro Swimming USA

http://www.usasynchro.org/

At this site you can read about Team USA and collegiate teams. Additionally you can find out about Synchro camps, resources, and more. Make sure you visit the Kick for Kids.

USA Swimming

http://www.usswim.org/

Through this website, you will be able to learn about this association and their activities, get statistical information on the swimmers from around the world, and get the latest schedule of events. Be sure to click on the SwimKids link for articles written for kids.

US Water Polo Inc.

http://www.usawaterpolo.com/uswp/

United States Water Polo, Inc., (USWP) is the national governing body for the sport of water polo in the United States. If you play water polo, visit this site for rules and regulations concerning the sport.

Sports
Tennis

Advantage Tennis Links

http://www.advantage-tennis.com/links.htm

If you are always searching for new tennis sites on the web, bookmark this page. There is an endless list of tennis sites bookmarked here and they are always being updated. You can even make suggestions for new sites to be listed.

Tennis One

http://www.tennisone.com/

Would you like to have the best game in tennis? Visit this site which contains the best of the best information on this sport. Take tennis lessons online, read about the pros, and get the latest ATP or WTA rankings.

The Tennis Server

http://www.tennisserver.com/

This site contains information on tennis equipment, the rules of tennis, the code of tennis, tennis clubs and organizations, and a tennis photo archive.

United States Tennis Association

http://www.usta.com/index.html

Find out what's happening in tennis by visiting this site. You will find standings, information on the US Open, Davis Cup, and the Olympics. Information is available on Juniors Tennis League and much more.

Sports
Track & Field

United States Youth Track and Field Association

http://www.USATF.org/youth/

There is a lot of information available on the result, schedules and other sites related to cross country/track and field events. You can also click on links from the parent organization.

Way Cool Running

http://www.waycoolrunning.com/

Way Cool Running is part of the Cool Running organization. At this site you will find information on youth running, including how and when to start a running program, how far, fast, and how often to run, and how and when to stretch.

Wilma Rudolph

http://www.donegal.k12.pa.us/dms/Kif/85/summarya.html

Wilma Rudolph, a renowned track and field star, had a great impact on the sport. Read about her accomplishments, the hurdles she overcame personally, and the effect she had upon the world.

Youth Runner Magazine

http://www.youthrunner.com/

This is a commercial magazine but there is plenty of information on this site. Read the Training Tips under articles. Find the schedules at the Calendar link.

Sports
Volleyball

United States Professional Volleyball

http://www.uspv.com/

Meet the girls who play on the U.S. Professional Volleyball team. While not a huge site, enthusiasts will find helpful information like player lists with their school affiliation, the coaches, and their schedule.

USA Volleyball

http://www.usavolleyball.org/

USA Volleyball is the national governing body for the sport of volleyball in the United States. At the site you can find information on teams, news, and download the rule fact sheets. Look for their youth program information.

Vball.com

http://www.Vball.com/

Vball.com is the complete online resource for the junior volleyball community brought to you by SportsNet. Designed for players, parents, club coaches, college coaches and fans, the site provides a variety of information for the junior volleyball community. Check out the Court Concepts for instructional articles.

Volleyball World Wide

http://www.volleyball.org/

Volleyball World Wide is a global source of information on the sport of volleyball. The site offers information on all aspects of the sport of volleyball—from beginner to professional, from high school to college to the Olympics.

Sports
Other Sports

American Canoe Association

http://www.acanet.org/acanet.htm

The ACA site provides information about canoeing and the organization's efforts to promote a safe sport and a quality environment. You can read the online magazine, which contains information from the print publication. Don't miss the Paddler Gallery to find beautiful photos.

Appalachian Trail Home Page

http://www.fred.net/kathy/at.html

Welcome to the world of camping along the Appalachian Trail. In addition to information about hiking and camping along this trail, this site contains information about camping in general.

Archery Network

http://archerynetwork.rivals.com/default.asp?sid=688

Okay, archery enthusiasts, this site is for you. You can sign up for a free archery newsletter, access information on equipment, and view videos about archery. Additionally, you can rate equipment, read the reviews, and use the message board.

CyberCamp

http://cybercamp.unl.edu

If you can't go away to a real camp, or if you just can't get enough of camp during the summer, then come here. You can get a list of items to make your own camping first-aid kit, read about nutrition, and get recipes. You can even sing camp songs around a virtual campfire.

Sports
Other Sports

GORP - Great Outdoor Recreation Page

http://www.gorp.com/

GORP is a virtual encyclopedia of information. Some of the information categories include: Destinations, Activities, Community, Travel, Gear, Books and Maps, Screensavers, Newsletters, and more. There is an entire library of articles from past editions of this site. Be sure to take time out to view the Video Gallery.

HBO Sports: World Championship Boxing

http://www.hbo.com/boxing/

Get the inside scoop, check out the ring chat, hear about the all-time greats, examine the sweet science, and see the HBO schedule.

Martial Arts for Kids

http://www.healthatoz.com/atoz/fitness/kidfit/kfmartialarts.asp

The martial arts are a great discipline and release of energy for participants. Information is provided on some of the martial arts including Tae kwon do, Jujitsu, Aikido, Judo, Karate, and Kung Fu.

National Archery Association

http://www.USArchery.org/naapub/fp/front.htm

There is so much information available to the archery enthusiast on this site. In addition to the Latest link and their calendar, find information on the coaches and participants.

Sports
Other Sports

OA Guide to Winter Camping

http://www.princeton.edu/~oa/winter/wintcamp.shtml

Have you ever thought about winter camping? This website presents useful information on this topic. For instance, do you know a how to build a shelter for yourself out of snow? There are eight shelters described here.

USA Gymnastics Online

http://www.usa-gymnastics.org/

USA Gymnastics Online is the official website of USA Gymnastics, a not-for-profit organization which is the governing body for the sport of gymnastics in the United States. At the site you'll find biographies of athletes and coaches, information about college gymnastics, fan mail, a guide to gymnastics, and much more.

USA Water Ski.org

http://usawaterski.org/index1.html

Keep up-to-date with the best water ski information. The site contains background information on this sport including barefoot, collegiate, show ski wakeboard, and ski racing. Check the Master Calendar for upcoming events.

US Figure Skating Online

http://www.usfsa.org/

Get all of the figure skating news at this site: results, information on athletes, clubs, and events. Submit questions to the Kids Question column and get a response from a skating celebrity. Also, there is "Ask Mr. Edge" for questions about your skating equipment.

Sports
Other Sports

Windsurfing - Beginners Guide

http://www.windsurfer.com/Beginners/index.html

Are you thinking about taking up windsurfing as your next sport? Come to this website and get background information, tips, equipment run-downs, and more. Even myths about the topic are covered.

World Championship Wrestling (WCW)

http://www.wcw.com/

At the official site of the WCW, you'll find news, results, wrestler bios, the Nitro report, multimedia, and more.

World Wresting Federation (WWF)

http://www.wwf.com/

This is the official site of the WWF. Along with bios of your favorite wrestling heroes, you'll find news, merchandise, media, and more. Link to the sights for The Rock, Stonecold, and WWF Divas.

Your Expedition

Http://www.yourexpedition.com/

Visit this site to learn about the extreme sport of adventuring across Antarctica. Two female explorers, Ann Bancroft (USA) and Liv Arnesen (Norway), are attempting to cross this ice mass by skiing and sailing. Read the polls, surveys and reports from the explorers.

States

50 States.com

http://www.50states.com/

This is the site for information on the 50 individual states. In addition to the statistical information provided, there are many links (approximately 60) to other information such as state flowers, historical monuments, highest point, flower, and flag. Note that there is a link to each state's home site.

NetState.com

http://www.netstate.com/states/index.html

With a page of information on every state, this site is an ideal reference for those state reports. Plus, find tables that list the 50 states and the date each was admitted into the Union, the ranking for each state for Per Capita Income, the ranking for each state for total area, total land area, and total inland water area in square miles.

U.S.A. CitiLink Project

http://banzai.neosoft.com/citylink/default.html

When you have to write a state report or you are planning a visit to a U.S. city, you will want to visit this useful and informative site. You can search for a city, or find a book about a city or state.

USA State Flags, Facts, Songs, Maps and Symbols

http://www.imagesoft.net/flags/usstate1.html

Click on the abbreviation for your state to see images of your state's flags, maps, and other information about states and symbols!

USA State Map/Quiz Printouts and Answers

http://www.enchantedlearning.com/usa/statesbw/

Calling all fifth graders! Are you learning state and capitals? This is the place to expand your knowledge. Click on a state and a map will appear along with questions that pertain to the map. Maps and questions are printable.

Alabama - AlaWeb

http://www.state.al.us/

Kids may need some help navigating this official site of the state of Alabama, but it's the best resource on the Web for information about the state.

Alaska Official Student Information Guide

http://www.dced.state.ak.us/tourism/student.htm

Everything you've always wanted to know about Alaska…and more! This site from the Alaska Division of Tourism tells kids the official symbols of Alaska, as well as some facts about the state, its history, and its government.

ArizonaGuide.com Just for Kids

http://www.arizonaguide.com/extra/kids/kidsindex.shtml

Did you know that Arizona became the 48th state on Valentine's Day? Learn Arizona facts, take a history tour, explore Arizona's natural wonders, and more at this kid-friendly site.

Arkansas

http://www.state.ar.us/ina/kids/arkids.html

Visit the Arkansas web site designed just for kids. You will find plenty to do here. Try the homework help or All About Arkansas, an especially helpful link for those of you writing a state report.

California Gold Rush Country

http://www.goldrush1849.com/

Information about the Gold Rush can be found at this site. They offer a Virtual Tour, background information, and many other links. It is worth the visit, but be aware that the writing is for older students.

All About Colorado: Kid Stuff

http://www.denver.org/visitors/kids.asp

Explore the rich history of the Wild West. Mingle with thousands of butterflies at the Butterfly Pavilion. Capture a breathtaking view of Denver atop the Twister rollercoaster at Six Flags Elitch Gardens Theme Park (if you can keep your eyes open!). These are just a few of the fun things to do in the Rocky Mountain State. Kids can also learn about the state symbols, government, and Denver at this site.

ConneCT Kids

http://www.kids.state.ct.us/

This site gives kids great facts about Connecticut's history, the state symbols, the government, and more. You can even try some puzzles and games while you're here.

Delaware's Kids' Page

http://www.state.de.us/kidspage/welcome.htm

Are you doing a report on Delaware or planning a vacation? Find Delaware facts, tour the governor's mansion, view Delaware wildlife photos, and more at this site that's specially designed for kids.

Florida Kids Page

http://dhr.dos.state.fl.us/kids/

This site leads to information that will help kids with their Florida projects and essays. Learn about people in Florida from 12,000 years ago to the present, and find out about the state flags, emblems, symbols, history facts, famous people, place names, and lots more.

ABC's of Georgia

http://tqjunior.thinkquest.org/5254/GEORGIA.HTM

This site made by talented and gifted 4th and 5th graders is a peach! It includes interesting places in the Atlanta area, places to visit outside of Atlanta, information about the historical battles in Georgia, and more fun facts.

Hawaii - Ahupua'a Adventure—From the Mountains to the Sea

http://tqjunior.thinkquest.org/3502/

The Ahupua'a Adventure game is designed to have people around the world learn more about Hawaii and its history and culture. Featured topics include medicinal plants, surfing, legends, beliefs, animal life, and recipes for some favorite Hawaiian foods.

Idaho: A Portrait

http://www.pbs.org/idahoportrait/

Explore the geography, the history, and the people of Idaho—the last state to be visited by American and European explorers. Embark on an interactive tour of the state's different regions and their vastly different landscapes. This PBS site will make you want to move to Idaho!

Discover Illinois

http://www.state.il.us/kids/default.htm

Illinois is the sixth most populous state in the country. Learn about the state symbols, capitols, and other interesting information by clicking on the state flag. Or, meet the governor, and read about bicycle safety, fire safety, and the environment.

Chicago

http://www.ash.udel.edu/incoming/east3/chicago/chicago.html

Would you like to learn about Chicago, Illinois—that "toddlin town?" This website on Chicago will lead you to many resources. Although this activity was designed for teams of students, the solo learner can benefit from the resources and the learning experience available at this site.

Indiana State Information Page

http://www.state.in.us/sic/about/

Get general Indiana facts, Indiana emblems, average climate information, and more. Be sure to visit the Little Hoosiers Kids Page for more kid-friendly state information.

Iowa Farmer Today's CornCam

http://www.iowafarmer.com/corncam/corn.html

The CornCam will returns to work each spring to record an Iowa cornfield from sunup to sunset. It will be on hand to chronicle the struggle of the little sprouts to break free of the surly bonds of earth and send shoots toward the sky. Experience an Iowa cornfield first hand!

Kansas Governor's Kids Page

http://www.state.ks.us/public/governor/govkids.html

Meet Governor Bill Graves at this site where he presents his state seal and symbols, a fun quiz, and other facts about Kansas.

The Commonwealth of Kentucky

http://www.uky.edu/KentuckyAtlas/kentucky.html

This informational site contains all the facts and history kids need to know about Kentucky, including the state bird, flower, fish, soil, and more.

Emblems of Louisiana

http://www.gatewayno.com/history/Emblems.html

Get Louisiana info from this no-nonsense site that shows the state bird, tree, dog, flower, seal, and flag.

Maine Kid's Page

http://www.state.me.us/sos/kids/

This state has put together an engaging web page that incorporates the state symbols and background information. You can listen to the state song and click a balloon for games. There are links to more in-depth information about the state.

Maryland Kid's Page

http://www.sos.state.md.us/sos/kids/html/kidhome.html

If you need to do a report on Maryland or if you just want to know more about the state, you're in luck! The state of Maryland created a great website for kids. You can learn about history, famous residents, government, and all you need to know.

Massachusetts Facts

http://www.state.ma.us/sec/cis/cismaf/mafidx.htm

Did you know that the chocolate chip cookie is the official cookie of Massachusetts? There's plenty more to learn about the Bay State at this detailed informational site.

Kids Discover Michigan

http://www.sos.state.mi.us/kidspage/index.html

Michigan history includes flashy cars, peace symbols and love beads, copper mining and coal barges, lighthouses, and the Sleeping Bear Dunes. This well-designed site has cool facts about Michigan's famous people, places, symbols, and government, and much more!

Michigan's Kids Pages

http://www.mda.state.mi.us/kids/

Created by the Michigan Department of Agriculture, this site has information that relates to farming—stories, pictures (e.g., look for 12-year-old Duke who makes maple syrup, and Rachel, 14, who tells about her life on a farm), and the State Fair.

Explore Minnesota Wildlife

http://www.dnr.state.mn.us/explore/index.html

Learn all about the frogs, toads, eagles, wolves, bears, and other amazing animals in Minnesota! This site includes tons of fun facts, news articles, and links.

Missouri River Quest

http://library.thinkquest.org/J001350/

The Missouri River Project is about the River's history, Lewis and Clark, steamboats, wildlife, and an experiment concerning its flow rate. The project presents information, challenges the user to a treasure hunt, provides quizzes to test the user's knowledge, and provides some fun through some crazy madlib generators.

Just for Kids (Missouri Department of Conservation)

http://www.conservation.state.mo.us/kids/

Missouri Frogs & Toads, Missouri Snakes, Leaf Invaders, and a fishing survey are some of the activities found on this site for children.

Montanakids.com

http://kids.state.mt.us/db_engine/subcat.asp?Subcat=State+Symbols

Montana has put together a kid-friendly and kid-fun site. It includes information about cities, counties, government, and statehood.

Nebraska Kids Page

http://gov.nol.org/Johanns/kids/

Send a message to Governor Johanns, learn about Nebraska state government, or take a online photo tour of the historic state capital building. This site also has a place to request a brochure and more detailed information if you are writing a report about Nebraska.

Nevada - Kids in Vegas

http://www.kidsinvegas.com/

Believe it or not, Las Vegas has lots of things for kids of all ages to do—from theme parks to arcades! Plus there is a lot to see and do all within a few hours' drive—every kid will remember taking a tour of the Grand Canyon, Hoover Dam, or Death Valley. Explore the site and find all the things for kids to do in Las Vegas.

New Hampshire Fall Foliage

http://www.visitnh.gov/framejump.php3?pagename=foliagereports.php3

Each year during foliage season, a statewide network of over 20 "leaf peepers" furnish the NH Division of Travel and Tourism with reports on the status of fall color. These reports cover the seven regions of the State. Visit this site to get the latest update on the Fall colors.

New Jersey Hangout

http://www.state.nj.us/hangout/

In addition to the regular state site stuff (found in "It's Your World"), this colorful site has art, music, games, a trip planner, a sports center, pet photos, a teen area, brain food, and more. Don't miss Professor Foulkii's cartoon history of New Jersey.

New Mexico

http://www.state.nm.us/Welcome.html

This official New Mexico site has links to everything a kid would ever need to know about the state. We suggest clicking the Fast Facts/Kid Stuff link for general information about the state flag, symbol, capital, etc.

New York: A Documentary Film Online

http://www.pbs.org/wnet/newyork/

Read about the documentary from PBS that explores the hidden parts of New York City. At this site you can take virtual reality tours of cool places, test your knowledge of the city, or read interviews with famous New Yorkers.

North Carolina Encyclopedia

http://statelibrary.dcr.state.nc.us/nc/cover.htm

This encyclopedia is designed to give you an overview of the people, the government, the history, and the resources of North Carolina. The information is organized into the broad information categories like history, geography, people, education, and more.

North Carolina Legends and Ghost Stories

http://www.secstate.state.nc.us/kidspg/legends.htm

The seven stories on this site all come from *North Carolina Legends* by Richard Walser. Fun reading for residents of the state!

Lewis & Clark in North Dakota

http://www.ndlewisandclark.com/

This stunning, informative site gives a closer look at the famous expedition in North Dakota. It takes a look at the preparations involved in the trip and the people on the expedition, and includes maps, trivia, and more.

Ohio Kids!

http://www.ohiokids.org/index.html

Try out the games, check out the kids area, or flip through Ohio History Central, an online encyclopedia all about Ohio's natural history and prehistory.

Oklahoma Home Page

http://www.oklaosf.state.ok.us/

This site isn't specifically for kids, but it does provide links to Oklahoma history and government information. Also includes links to popular Oklahoma sites.

Umatilla, Oregon

http://www.ccrh.org/comm/umatilla/begin.htm

This Web site, a "virtual exhibit," tells the story of Umatilla, Oregon, since the building of the "big" dams on the Columbia River. Umatilla's history is told through the words of its residents and neighbors, and through photographs, legislation, and historic documents.

Pennsylvania - Historic Philadelphia

http://www.ushistory.org/tour/

Enjoy a virtual tour of the historical riches found within one square mile in Historic Philadelphia—from the Liberty Bell to the Man Full of Trouble Tavern. Learn a little history, catch wise to some architecture, and pick up fascinating morsels of trivia for that state report!

Rhode Island

http://www.rilin.state.ri.us/studteaguide/tcaguide.html

This site is an online resource for students who wish to increase their knowledge of the Rhode Island State House, as well as Rhode Island's history and government.

South Carolina - MySCGov.com

http://www.state.sc.us/

The goal of this website is to provide quick and easy access to all aspects of South Carolina Government, as well as links to other local, county, and national sites. You can get the latest state news, see the weather in different parts of South Caroline, and more.

South Dakota

http://www.travelsd.com/history/sioux/sioux.htm

Learn about the legendary spots in South Dakota and read about the treasures, art, and culture you might find if you visit this great Sioux nation.

State of Tennessee Kids Pages

http://www.state.tn.us/kids.html

Link to the Department of Health's "Healthy Kids" page with games, puzzles, an art gallery, and a coloring book, all aimed at showing you how to stay healthy and safe. Or, visit the Department of Education's page for students with links to Tennessee facts, symbols, and more.

Texas Senate Kids and the Governor's Kids Pages

http://www.senate.state.tx.us/kids/

http://www.governor.state.tx.us/kids/

Texas has two sites for kids. One is Senate Kids, which helps kids understand what state government is all about. There are two levels of use—For Kids and Senate Jr., designed for younger cowpolks to use with their parents help. The second site (click on the Kids Page link) provides information on the state and a greeting from the Governor.

Discover Utah!

http://www.infowest.com/Utah/index.html

Whether you want to learn more about Dinosaurland, Castle Country, or Great Salt Lake Country, this site is for you. It provides information about each section of Utah.

Vermont Home Page

http://www.state.vt.us/index.htm

This official Vermont site isn't flashy, but it does contain many helpful links to everything from Vermont ski conditions to *Vermont Life* magazine.

Virginia Online Legislature

http://legis.state.va.us./vaonline/v.htm

This site contains the symbols and emblems of the Commonwealth, as well as a Kids Korner with virtual tours, an activity center, trivia, and more.

Washington Apples

http://www.bestapples.com/

Did you know Washington apples are the best apples on earth? Well, that's what they claim. This site has crop facts, kids pages, and a slide show of historical Washington apple industry photos from the "Apple Collection" at the North Central Washington Museum.

Cameras Over Washington, D.C.

http://photo2.si.edu/aerialdc/aerialdc.html

This Web page is fun to look at! It contains aerial views of Washington, DC, including the Capitol, the Washington Monument, and the Lincoln and Jefferson Memorials.

West Virginia Kids' Page

http://www.legis.state.wv.us/kids/kids.html

This online activity book has fun facts about the state, matching games, a directory of state symbols, and more. Very informative for school reports.

Wisconsin.gov Kids Page

http://www.wisconsin.gov/state/core/kids_page.html

Want to learn more about the state of Wisconsin? Follow the links on this site to various pages with games, trivia, and other cool stuff. Don't miss the site sponsored by the Wisconsin State Senate, which includes information about the state, how bills become law, and the capitol building.

Wyoming Kid's Page

http://www.state.wy.us/kids.html

This simple site tells kids everything they need to know about Wyoming and includes Wyoming stories and wildlife information.

Cheyenne, Wyoming

http://business.lcc.whecn.edu/cheyenne/

Try this site if you would like to know what life is like in Wyoming country. You can visit more than 90 museum within the state, take virtual tours, and more. You will come away with a great understanding of the West.

Teens

A+ Research and Writing

http://www.ipl.org/teen/aplus/

This site for high school and college students will help with super research papers.
Begin with the Step by Step—a guide to researching and writing a paper. Next do
the Info Search, about finding information in cyberspace and in your library. Use
the links as online resources for research and writing.

Chapter One

http://www.washingtonpost.com/wp-dyn/style/books/

Have you ever thought you would like to read a newly released book, but you just
were not sure if you would like it? At this site you can read the first chapter of a
recent release and also read a review of the book from the Washington Post. Click
on Chapter One on their Book World page.

The Concord Review

http://www.tcr.org

If you have high standards for your academic work and if you are interested in
history, then you will like this site. High school students can submit a research
paper on a history topic to the Concord Review for publication. The paper goes
through the usual editing process that any journal requires. If published, the paper
becomes a resume enhancement for college applications.

CosmoGirl

http://www.cosmogirl.com/

This magazine, a relative of the famed *Cosmopolitan*, has been designed just for
teen girls. In addition to the usual columns, you can find information on modeling
requirements, contributing to the magazine (teen contributors are chosen twice a
year), submitting a room makeover, and so much more.

GovTeen

http://www.govteen.com/

Here is a site that has many aspects to it. If you need help with a technical problem, here is the place to seek an answer. You can join a chat room or put a question or comment on the forum. There is a game room and an art center where you can see great graphic designs, drawings, poems, and stories, all created and submitted by teen members.

Guess

http://www.guess.com/

If you're a fashion diva, you will like this site. Click on the Guess Spot and you can get information on fashion and new trends, models, behind-the-scene news, and more. Since fashion tends to be seasonal, check back here often.

HighWiredSports.com

http://www.highwired.com/HWS

Keep up-to-date with the latest sports new by frequenting this site. You can look at the sports news by region or by sport. Find the national ranking or who was signed and by which team.

I.P.L. Teen Division

http://www.ipl.org/teen/

Not many teen sites are as comprehensive as this one. There are many links to help you be the best you can be—Career Pathways, College and Careers, Money Matters, Dating and Stuff, etc. Of course there are the usual library study links, too.

Nutrition on the Web for Teens

http://library.thinkquest.org/10991/

This site brings nutrition information to the adolescent. Learn the basics of exercise, find out how poverty affects nutrition in other countries, read about some of the most common health myths, or get low-fat recipes to help you lose weight.

LAYouth

http://www.layouth.com

This site is a publication written by teens for teens. While aimed at Los Angeles teens, other teens might find this site interesting. Features of the online publication include teen services, entertainment, contests, cool links, and more.

New Expression Online

http://www.newexpression.org/

New Expression Online is a publication presented by Chicago teens. In addition to current news events, there is usually a focus story. You will also find entertainment, Face-Off, features, This 'n That, and more.

NoodleBib 2.0 (A Free Online Bibliography Maker)

http://www.noodletools.com/

You are getting ready to write a paper and you don't know how to properly list the references you are using. This free online program will help you to do that. All you have to do is click on NoodleBib and select the reference type from the pull-down menu.

React.com

http://www.react.com/

This is a fun site that will engage the user. You will find polls (e.g., Do you have a brattitude?), movie information, news and sports, games, and shopping. Be sure to check out the Useful Stuff link.

ResearchPaper.com

http://www.researchpaper.com/

Need a research or speech topic? This site can help. At ResearchPaper.com there are over 4000+ topic ideas. In addition, you will find resources for researching the paper, project, or speech.

SERVEnet.org

http://www.servenet.org/

This site is the premier website on service and volunteering. Through SERVEnet users can enter their zip code, city, state, skills, interests, and availability and be matched with organizations needing help. SERVEnet is also a place to search for calendar events, job openings, service news, recommended books, and best practices.

Seventeen

http://www.seventeen.com

When you arrive at this site, try the links on the left side—Chat & Chill, Beauty, Fashion, Body and Sports, etc. You can also take their poll, read the feature articles, or customize the site to fit your own interests.

TeenHangout.com

http://teenhangout.studentcenter.org/

This really is a teen hangout. You can chat, see who is online, and join forums. At the left side of the screen you will find other teen related sites—movies, music, jokes, poetry, horoscopes, idols, sports, diaries, and more.

Teen Ink

http://www.teenink.com/

Here is a publication that is written by teens for teens. Categories include non-fiction, fiction, poetry, reviews, art, sports, and more. A special college area contains a college directory, college essays, articles, and reviews of schools. There are no staff writers so they are looking for submissions from their readers.

TeenLine

http://www.teenlineonline.org/tabled.html

Do you need help? If you are a teenager, you can call this site for help with personal problems. Although it is based in the Los Angeles area, teens from all over the country can call/e-mail to get help. This site is run by trained teens and is affiliated with Cedars Sinai Medical Center.

TeenPeople Online

http://www.teenpeople.com

Stars, style, games, buzz, get personal, chat, and contests are just some of the great sections that you will find at this site. Take the latest poll and read the results. The site looks best if you have Flash on your computer.

TeenVoice.com

http://www.teenvoice.com/

This site is created by teens and is written for teens. Sections of the site include: Realtime News, TheZone Sports, Entertainment, Xpressions Gallery, Teen Fashion, and Guidance. We liked the Xpressions Gallery, a place where you can submit photographs, essays and articles, and seek advice.

Yahoo! Get Local

http://local.yahoo.com/

Find out what going on in your city at this website. Or if you are planning a vacation, know what is happening in your vacation city before you arrive. This site can provide information about movie theaters, restaurants, shopping, cultural events, and more.

WebCrawler - Teens

http://www.webcrawler.com/kids_and_family/teens/

This site created just for teens is teeming with links. Try the "Generation in Circuit" link, a zine written for, by, and about young people. Collect information on life from "Go Ask Alice." Visit the "Grip Magazine" link and find out how to become a feature writer or artist. There is plenty more…

The Why Files

http://whyfiles.org

The Why Files cover science, health, environment, and technology issues from a unique perspective. Using news and current events as a springboard to explore science and the larger issues it raises, they hope to show science as a human enterprise and a way of looking at the world. There is always an in-depth and an in-brief article.

Weather

El Niño: The Baby That Won't Behave

http://www.ash.udel.edu/incoming/mbasch/intro.html

Steven Spielberg is planning a movie shoot and he has to know if El Niño will effect the shooting schedule. Your job is to study up on El Niño and help him decide on the best location. Have fun as you learn about this weather phenomenon.

Intellicast - World and Local Weather

http://www.mapquest.com/

Intellicast provides extensive specialized weather information to help plan all outdoor and weather sensitive activities, whether you're hiking, skiing, or relaxing at the beach. Drawing on the meteorological knowledge of its staff, this site provides over 250,000 pages of detailed weather information.

Weather Cam

http://www.earthcam.com/cgi-bin/search_cam.cgi?subject:WEA;file:WEA

Click on this site and see the weather around the world. If you have relatives living or visiting an area of the world different from you own, wouldn't you like to see what they are experiencing? With the weather cam you can see more than 700 sites from around the world.

The Weather Channel Home Page

http://www.weather.com/

Need the latest weather information? This site provides local, national, and international weather information. Check out the Storm Watch, maps, and forecasts. One of the nice features of this site is the news on how the weather is affecting events around the world.

Web Resources
Browsers & Plug-Ins

Many of the sites included in this book require plug-ins so you can access all of their features. Plug-ins are software programs that extend the capabilities of your browser, giving you the ability to play games, view video movies, listen to music, and more. Most popular plug-ins are free to download and easy to install on your computer. Downloading a plug-in may take a little extra time, but the enhancements you'll get are well worth the wait! The most common plug-ins are listed below.

Adobe Acrobat

http://www.adobe.com/prodindex/acrobat/readstep.html

Many downloadable documents are saved as Adobe Acrobat files (also referred to as PDF format). In order to view these files on your computer, you need Acrobat Reader. You can go to this site and download the free version. Acrobat Reader on enables you to view and print Acrobat files. If you want to post a document as an Acrobat file, you would need the full version of Adobe Acrobat, which must be purchased.

Internet Explorer

http://www.microsoft.com/downloads/

When you arrive at this Microsoft site you will have to use the pull-down menu to find the right version of the browser for your computer. Internet Explorer is free, but you can also download other Microsoft programs from here for a fee.

Macromedia Shockwave & Macromedia Flash
http://sdc.shockwave.com/shockwave/download/

Macromedia Shockwave and Macromedia Flash Players let you experience the most engaging, interactive content on the web. Follow the three simple steps on this site to quickly get these free web players. When you download the Macromedia Shockwave Player, you'll automatically get the Flash Player as well.

Netscape

http://home.netscape.com/computing/download/index.html

Get the latest versions of the Netscape browsers at this site. Click on the Netscape Browsers link, then choose which browser version you want. The site will guide you through the download and installation process.

Netscape Plug-Ins

http://home.netscape.com/plugins/index.html

To extend the capabilities of your Netscape browser, visit this site to download most of the available plug-ins. You can search by type of plug-in and by computer platform (e.g., Windows, Macintosh).

RealAudio

http://www.realaudio.com/

In order to hear most music on websites or use an online radio, you'll need a RealAudio Player. There isn't a fee to download the latest version of RealPlayer. This site will guide you through the download and installation process.

QuickTime

http://www.apple.com/quicktime/download/

QuickTime is Apple's technology for handling video, sound, animation, graphics, text, music, and VR scenes. It's available for both Mac and PC at this site for free. Simply sign up and mark what type of computer you are using. There is a help section to guide you through the installation process.

Web Resources
Computer Education

About the Internet

http://www.bpl.org/WWW/KIDS/AboutInternet.html

This website provides lots of information about the Internet. In fact, it even shows how it works. Terms like TCP/IP, WWW, links, browser, and ISP are discussed. If you read this page, you will have a pretty good idea of what the Internet is.

CNET

http://www.Cnet.com/

This is THE source for computing and technology. There is news, computer hardware and software information, pricing, and much, much more. Use the directory or search to find the information you need.

Personal Computers: Inside and Out

http://library.thinkquest.org/15793/

This site is designed to help students learn about personal computers: how they work, their various parts, and their history. The computer's functions, a vocabulary of terms, operating systems, hardware, a historical time line, and a bibliography page all help users obtain a better understanding of this subject. An image map will also help students understand the inner workings of a computer. Different types of computer viruses are also discussed.

TechWeb

http://www.techweb.com/encyclopedia/

Are you looking for the definition of a technology term that you just don't understand? Try this site. At the first screen type in your term and find the definition. It is a great help when trying to understand those files that you need to run some program.

The Revolutionaries

http://www.thetech.org/revolutionaries/

This site highlights the major contributors to the technology age from Nolan Bushnell, the founder of Atari, to Gordon Moore of Intel. Read the information at this site and you will have insight on the computer revolution.

The Tech PC Webopedia

http://thetech.pcwebopedia.com

Need to define a technology term but can't find it in the dictionary? Words are being "coined" so fast that it is hard to keep track of them. This site is doing just that with 4000 in their Webopedia. Put the word or phrase in and do a search or look for words according to topic.

Web Teacher

http://www.webteacher.org/macnet/welcome.html

Anything you could possibly want to learn about the World Wide Web is available at this site. This site is appropriate for the beginner who wants to know the basics of how to use the web, the intermediate user who wants to dabble with creating a web page, or the advanced user who wants to know more about Java, CGI, and adding movies.

WebTips for Children

http://www.EnchantedLearning.com/Webtipsforchildren.html

If you want to give a child with no web experience a little background, turn him loose on this page. It gives the basics about the components of a web page: the mouse, links, scrolling, resizing windows, etc.

Web Resources
Community

AOL Instant Messenger

http://www.aol.com/aim/

The AOL Instant Messenger service is a great way to talk to your friends on the Internet—in real time. You do not need to be an AOL member to download and use Instant Messenger.

eBoard

http://www1.eboard.com

Would you like a place to post messages for either yourself or for your friends and family to see? Maybe you would like to post pictures of your class filed trip, your vacation, or your last birthday party. eBoard is the place you can do this without having to create a web page.

ICQ

http://www.icq.com

ICQ is a user-friendly Internet tool that informs you who's online at any time and enables you to contact them at will. ICQ searches for your list of friends, alerting you in real time when they log on. With ICQ, you can chat, send messages, files and URLs, play games, or just hang out with your fellow 'Netters' while still surfing the Net. You need to download software to use this.

QuickDot

http://www.quickdot.com

Quickdot is a fast, easy way to connect with people online. It combines the best aspects of email with a wireless messaging service. QuickDot message spaces are just right for fast, informal notes to your family, friends, project team, etc.

ToadMail

http://www.twotoads.com

ToadMail is a free, filtered web-based email. The email works just like any other email, but with one big exception…all of the incoming and outgoing mail is scanned by proprietary filtering software for inappropriate words or language. You can sign up for this service at this site. Parents are encouraged to be included in the sign-up process.

Yahoo! Groups

http://groups.yahoo.com/

Yahoo! Groups, now merged with eGroups, is a free group email service that offers a convenient way for you to connect with others who share the same interests and ideas. When you sign up a group, you get one email address and a website that allows you to share photos and files, plan events, send a newsletter, or just stay in touch. Join an existing group to discuss sports, health, current events, and more.

Yahoo! Mail

http://mail.yahoo.com/

Need an email address? Sign up with Yahoo! Mail and store up to 6 MB of messages for free. You'll be able to access your email from anywhere with this convenient account.

Yahoo! Messenger

http://messenger.yahoo.com/

Instant messaging allows you to quickly exchange messages with your online friends. Unlike email, instant messages appear as soon as they're sent. By downloading the Yahoo! Messenger application to your computer, you can send instant messages

Web Resources
Copyright, Netiquette & Safe Surfing

Art Rights and Wrongs

http://library.thinkquest.org/J001570/

Kids making websites will need to understand why copyrights, trademarks, and licenses are important. With digital media so easy to obtain, it is often thought that means it is free. This site attempts to straighten out the misconception about copyright laws and how it effects kids' webpage design. If you are a web designer or aspire to be one, don't miss this!

Netiquette for Kids

http://www.bpl.org/WWW/KIDS/Netiquette.html

The Boston Public Library has posted this site for kids. There are good ideas here for everyone, no matter what their age.

SurfMonkey Internet Safety

http://www.surfmonkey.com/company/surfing_code.asp

Read the Top Secret Surfing Code found on this site. You will feel a lot safer if you give these ideas some thought and if you practice them all of the time.

Ten Commandments of Computer Ethics

http://www.cpsr.org/program/ethics/cei.html

The Ten Commandments of Computer Ethics are a good reminder of how to use technology in the right way. It might be a good idea to print a copy to hang near your computer.

Web Resources
Kid-Safe Directories & Search Engines

This section contains what are considered to be kid-safe search engines. However, even with these search engines, inappropriate sites can emerge. We suggest that kids should always be supervised by a parent or caretaker when they are online.

Awesome Library

http://www.awesomelibrary.org/

The Awesome Library organizes the Web with 15,000 carefully reviewed resources, including the top 5 percent in education. There are more than 20 topic areas in which kids can search. Click on the Kids section when you arrive at the home page.

Ask Jeeves for Kids

http://www.ajkids.com/

This site allows children to search for information in a kid-safe environment. It is easy to use because of the real language approach to searching. In other words, you can actually type in a question and it will interpret it and come back with suggested sites.

Bess - The Internet Retriever

http://www.bess.net/

Kids can surf the Internet in this safe-surfing environment. There is a directory of information for kids to use initially. If you can't find the information there, then look for the Searchopolis link for a more in-depth search.

Berit's Best Websites

http://www.beritsbest.com/

This is another directory site for finding information. If you can't find the information within the directory, there is a search mechanism where specific key words can be input. Students can make suggestions for site to be included in the directory.

KidsClick

http://sunsite.berkeley.edu/KidsClick!/

At this site, created by public librarians for children, the user will find more that 600 links to information sources. KidsClick is updated regularly by the librarians and the all of the sites posted on it are chosen for their appropriateness for children.

SurfMonkey

http://www.surfmonkey.com

SurfMonkey is a kid safe websurfing environment. You can download for free the Surf Monkey Bar, a small, compact "cyber shield" that resides at the bottom of the Internet Explorer window. It automatically filters out inappropriate sites and only allows access to child-safe sites. Updating is automatic. Read the compatibility requirements for more detailed information.

Teach-nology

http://www.teach-nology.com/mega_search/10_search_engines/

This site offers a bunch of search engines that are suitable for children. In fact, this site can be used as a portal, which you can set in your browser as your default opening page. Some of the engines include: 4anything.com, Infospace, Go.com, and AskJeeves, but there are plenty more.

Yahooligans

http://www.yahooligans.com/

Try this great web guide for kids. Do you want to know about movies, games, sports, and school subjects? This is a great place to begin your search. There is a directory of information and a regular search engine.

Web Resources
Other Directory & Search Engines

Alta Vista
http://www.altavista.digital.com

Direct Hit
http://www.directhit.com

DogPile
http://www.dogpile.com

Excite
http://www.excite.com

Google
http://www.google.com

GoTo.com
http://www.goto.com

HotBot
http://hotbot.lycos.com/

Lycos
http://www.lycos.com/

Magellan
http://magellan.excite.com/

Mamma
http://www.mamma.com

MetaCrawler
http://www.metacrawler.com

MSN
http://www.msn.com/

NBCi
http://www.nbci.com/

Northern Light
http://www.northernlight.com

SmallShop
http://www.smallshop.com

Yahoo!
http://www.yahoo.com

Web Resources
Web Page Design

CustomPost

http://www.custompost.com/

This is a free message board that can be added to your own web page. One of the nice features of this board is you can add icons to show mood, which is something most boards do not have.

Domain Search

http://www.vsconnect.com/whois/

If you have created a web page and want to post it with your own domain name, check with this site. You will have to purchase the use of the name: domain names are not usually free.

The Express Page

http://www.expage.com/

Would you like to create and post your own web page? Express page offers free homepages for all users of the World Wide Web. In fact, they house over 8,249,592 pages! The great benefit to this site is you can get all of the HTML help that you need in the Help section.

Learning HTML

http://www.ipl.org/youth/kidsweb/

Do you want to learn how to create a web page? This site is the place to begin. Begin by learning what HTML means. Follow the examples given and use some of the graphics links they provide. If you are patient, you will have your very own web page. Once you get it posted, submit the URL to this site for possible inclusion.

Lissa Explains it All

http://www.lissaexplains.com/

Would you like to create a web page? Come to Lissa's site and you will learn how.
She has a knack for teaching kids the art of using HTML. If you are new at it, go
to Basic and start with Section 1. If you are more advanced, then go to the area
that you want to learn about—frames, tables, CSS, and more. Don't miss the
tools—there are goodies hidden in there!

School City

http://www.schoolcity.com/

School City offers many benefits for schools, teachers, and students. One of the
most useful elements is the free website space and the website builder. Students
can create presentation websites and post them here.

Web Developers Virtual Library

http://www.stars.com

This is an indispensable site when you are trying to get that first home page up and
running and an even better resource once you get hooked on HTML and want to
start doing the fancy things.

WebQuest
Web Kids' Village

http://www.ks-connection.org/village/village.html

This section is a place where children can find personal homepages created by
other kids. It is intended to be a kids' community in the form of an electronic
village. If you have a kid-created webpage, you can put a link on this site.

Notes